Empowering African-American Males

THIS WORKBOOK BELONGS TO:

_____

MYCHAL WYNN

Empowering African-American Males

TEACHER, PARENT, & MENTOR
WORKBOOK

RISING SUN
PUBLISHING

EMPOWERING AFRICAN-AMERICAN MALES

TEACHER, PARENT, & MENTOR WORKBOOK

ISBN 1-880463-71-7
Copyright © 2005 Mychal Wynn
Copyright © 2005 Rising Sun Publishing, Inc.

The poems, *Born to Win, Be A Winner, A Man Is,* and *A Pledge to Myself* are reprinted from the book, ***Don't Quit – Inspirational Poetry*** copyright 1990 by Mychal Wynn. The poems, *What Manner of Men Are We ..., A Parent's Vision, Remembering from Whence We Came,* and *What I Won't Do for My Friends* are reprinted by permission of the author.

Credits:
Cover design by Mychal Wynn.
Student Photographs taken by Mychal Wynn.
Stock Photographs by Fotosearch.

Reference sources for style and usage: *The New York Public Library Writer's Guide to Style and Usage* copyright 1994 by The New York Public Library and the Stonesong Press, Inc., and the *APA Stylebook 2004* by the Associated Press.

RISING SUN
PUBLISHING
P.O. Box 70906
Marietta, GA 30007-0906
770.518.0369/800.524.2813
FAX 770.587.0862
E-mail: info@rspublishing.com
Web site: http://www.rspublishing.com

Printed in the United States of America.

Acknowledgments

I would like to thank those parents, educators, counselors, and mentors who have embraced this book and who are working diligently to turn the tide against seemingly insurmountable odds to help Black males experience school success as they discover their role in pursuing the American Dream.

A special thank you to my friends—editor, Dr. Glenn Bascome, a classroom teacher and Director of the Dame Marjorie Bean Education Center in Somerset, Bermuda and an excellent role model; and Karen McCord, a Professor at Solano Community College, for her thoughts and insight. I would also like to convey my sincere appreciation to Ella Tolliver, Vilma France, Ethel Cook-Wilson, Donald Sanders, and Curtis McCord for their support in proofreading the text.

My wife, Nina, who has always been there to protect our sons from the many challenges, obstacles, and pitfalls which claim the spirits of Black males each school day.

I would like to acknowledge and thank all the teachers, coaches, counselors, administrators, friends, family, and mentors who have contributed to the growth, development, nurturing, and maturation of our sons. Nowhere is it more evident, "It takes a village to raise a child," than in raising and nurturing a Black male from boyhood to manhood.

Finally, I would like to acknowledge my mother, father, family, and community, who nurtured, prayed for, guided, and protected me. I recognize too, Mr. Roberts, my fifth- and sixth-grade teacher, at Edmund Burke Elementary School, who inspired learning; Dr. Cheryl Gholar, my high school job placement counselor, at Du Sable High School, who held out hope for my future; and Mrs. Ernestine Whiting, Dean Roland Latham, Harvette Emmett, and the professors at Northeastern University, who helped me defy the odds in becoming the first college graduate in my family. I also thank my former and present pastors, Dr. Frederick K.C. Price, Dr. Creflo A. Dollar, and the Reverend Kenneth Marcus, all of whom have nurtured my spirit and led me into a deeper understanding of God's Word and his expectations of me as a husband, father, and believer.

Dedication

To my wife, for her patience, understanding, and support, and to my sons, Mychal-David and Jalani, who represent the promise and potential of Black males.

Table of Contents

About the Author

Mychal Wynn brings the issues pertaining to Black male achievement to the forefront of educational, community, and household discussions. From his humble beginnings in rural Pike County, Alabama, to the second-grade teacher who told his mother, "I doubt if he will ever make it beyond elementary school;" to becoming an internationally-acclaimed author and educational consultant; his life experiences provide insight into, and an understanding of, the challenges confronting Black student achievement in general, and Black male achievement in particular.

Despite numerous office referrals, suspensions throughout elementary and middle school, and being expelled from Chicago's De La Salle Catholic High School, Mychal Wynn, graduated with honors from Boston's Northeastern University; co-founded, together with his wife, Rising Sun Publishing; and has written over sixteen books which explore issues ranging from school improvement and parental involvement to closing the student achievement gap and paving the way for increasing the number of Black males matriculating into college.

At the original publication of this book under the title, *Empowering African-American Males to Succeed: A Ten-Step Approach for Parents and Teachers (1992)*, his older son was four years old. He is now sixteen, and together with his younger brother (ten years old), their academic success, standardized test scores, and personal achievement represent the promise and potential of Black males. For over two decades, Mr. Wynn has been an advocate for children—provoking discussion, providing training, and publishing books and materials which provide insight, strategies, and solutions to the myriad of problems hindering Black male achievement from primary through postsecondary school.

He, his wife, Nina, and their two sons, Mychal-David and Jalani (both of whom attend public schools), reside in Georgia.

Foreword

When the *Empowering African-American Males Succeed: A Ten-Step Approach for Parents and Teachers* book and workbook were published in 1992, I wholly anticipated they would be adopted by every urban school district in America and regularly referred to by classroom teachers, who, throughout the country, were struggling in their efforts to help Black males become academically and socially successful. In 1992, my wife and I had one son, who was four years old and attending preschool at the First Lutheran Church in Carson, California. At home she and I were doing with him everything outlined in the book. Our older son is now sixteen years old and in the eleventh grade at North Springs High School in Atlanta, Georgia. My wife and I have another son, currently ten years old and in the fifth grade. Their academic achievement and social development are the result of the strategies outlined in the original book, additional strategies contained within this book, and relationships with coaches, teachers, principals, pastors, and mentors who have provided their much-needed web of protection. However, they are the exceptions rather than the rule as Black males in public education continue to be disproportionately placed into special education, disproportionately suspended from school, disproportionately dropping out of school, and virtually at the bottom of the academic achievement gap in every category (i.e., reading, writing, math, and science).

In Nathan and Julia Hare's book, *Bringing the Black Boy to Manhood: The Passage,* they note:

> *The Black race is like an unsteady palace, gigantic and ornate, teetering at*
> *its base while people gather around with cranes and complex machinery.*
> *The people squeal and squelch and prop the palace up, feverishly, pompously,*
> *working to repair it at its cracks and wobbly ceiling, when all the while the*
> *problem of the building's unsteadiness is a few missing bricks and broken*
> *mortar from its now all but invisible foundation.*

Enabling and empowering Black males requires a few missing bricks (mission, vision, climate & culture, curriculum & content, instruction, and assessment) and renewed mortar (strong relationships, effective collaboration, focus, and direction). In my hope to better assist teachers and serve parents,

I have revised the original book and workbook, providing more strategies, expanding the activities, and providing current census and achievement data. Together, they represent integral components of a larger vision of developing personal empowerment, college aspirations, college planning, and inspiring young men to look beyond their current circumstances to future possibilities. While I have used my family's experiences to illustrate points, I empathize with the added struggles of the many single-parent households raising Black males. However, if single-parents are successful in forming a web of protection and support in response to their unique struggles, I believe that they can replicate our successes.

The most difficult task facing educators, parents, and mentors of Black males in the United States, Bermuda, the Caribbean, Canada, Europe, and Africa is to expand their focus beyond intervention and prevention programs to conceptualizing and implementing empowerment processes. Increasing reading and math scores is not a lofty enough aspiration. Envisioning a young man becoming an entrepreneur; CEO of Merrill Lynch, AOL Time Warner, or American Express; neurosurgeon, research scientist, or head of government provides a framework for learning how to do (i.e., run things) rather than how to get by (i.e., achieve proficiency).

The original version of this book outlined ten building blocks dealing with the critical areas required to build stronger relationships with Black males as part of the transformation of their thinking from excuses to empowerment and from low-performance to high academic achievement. The information contained within those building blocks has been woven into the six components as presented in the book, *Increasing Student Achievement: Volume I, Vision:* Mission, Vision, Climate & Culture, Curriculum & Content, Instruction, and Assessment. The components are dealt with from the perspective of overall school improvement through the systemic changes, cultural shift, operational teams, and research needed to pave the way to higher achievement levels for all students. Here, the components are dealt with from the perspective of the unique needs of Black males and their families as part of a holistic set of strategies directed at closing the achievement gap and successfully empowering Black males to move through the K-12 educational system into postsecondary institutions.

Mychal Wynn

How to use this book

This workbook have been designed to be used in support of the ideas, suggestions, and strategies raised in the book. As such, it is highly suited to support workshops, staff development sessions, book clubs, and parenting seminars. Depending on your respective role (e.g., parent or teacher), you may be in a position to apply the strategies directly to the teaching and child-rearing of Black males. As a superintendent, principal, or program director, you may be in a position to sensitize parents, teachers, mentors, coaches, and school counselors to the information in hopes of enhancing their relationships with Black males and better understanding the needs of families, thereby paving the way to higher academic achievement and fewer discipline problems. Coaches, counselors, and mentors will expand their knowledge and understanding of the unique issues confronting Black males and their families as they navigate their way through an oftentimes confusing primary-through-postsecondary educational system.

The book upon which the workbook is based raises as many questions as it provides insight—beginning with defining your role, conceptualizing your mission, and clarifying your vision. As an adult stakeholder, you are challenged with answering the questions, "If not me, who? If not now, when?" As much as possible, the author and editor, both Black men (one a Black American, the other, a Black Bermudian), have attempted to depersonalize the issues. However, both are fathers who have worked diligently to overcome the very issues outlined within this book to ensure the academic, social, spiritual, and emotional nurturing of their children. The editor, Dr. Glenn Bascome (a public school teacher), and his wife have seen their two children graduate from college—their daughter is a public school teacher with a Master's degree and their twenty-five-year-old son expects to complete his doctorate in physiotherapy in 2006. The author, Mychal Wynn, and his wife continue to encounter the issues raised in this book as their sons are currently in high school and elementary school.

This book sets forth a process, as outlined in the book *Increasing Student Achievement: Volume I, Vision*, where each Chapter builds upon strategies set forth in each preceding Chapter. The *Key Points* following each Chapter in the book have been reprinted here together with activities designed to further operationalize the ideas and strategies set forth in the accompanying Chapter of the book.

While the book and workbook have been written to specifically address issues relating to Black males, you will find the approach used and strategies provided relate to all children. Whether you are a parent, teacher, coach, counselor, principal, or mentor, you must become a role player in influencing change within your school community. Becoming an advocate for children will require that you no longer wait for new leadership, new programs, or new research. You must become the catalyst to move ideas and strategies beyond discussions to being operationalized.

The "Web of Protection" illustrated in Chapter four, *Curriculum & Content*, will help each role player to understand the importance of communication and collaboration. Strong relationships between role players are paramount to protecting Black males from the many issues threatening their lives and contributing to their lack of academic achievement, unemployment, and high rates of incarceration.

Finally, while the book and workbook will explore many of the most plaguing issues, the following books are recommended as additional resources to assist your efforts in developing a comprehensive set of strategies designed to identify a young man's gifts, inspire his dreams, and provide him with a primary-through-postsecondary plan:

- *Ten Steps to Helping Your Child Succeed in School*
- *A Middle School Plan for Students with College-Bound Dreams*
- *A High School Plan for Students with College-Bound Dreams*
- *Follow Your Dreams: Lessons That I Learned in School*
- *The Eagles who Thought They were Chickens*

Schoolhouses do not teach themselves—
piles of brick and mortar and machinery
do not send out men. It is strengthened by
long study and thought, that breathes the
real breath of life into boys and girls and
makes them human.

— W.E.B. DuBois

Empowering African-American Males

verview

Working with Black Males

The pain is in the eyes. Young Black men in their late twenties or early thirties living in urban American, lost and abandoned, aimlessly walking and hawking the streets with nothing behind their eyes but anger, confusion, disappointment and pain ...

— *Haki R. Madhubuti*

This workbook has been designed to support the book, *Empowering African-American Males: Teaching, Parenting, and Mentoring Successful Black Males*. The activities also relate to the six components outlined in the book, *Increasing Student Achievement: Volume I, Vision* (Mission, Vision, Climate & Culture, Curriculum & Content, Instruction, & Assessment). As a parent, teacher, counselor, coach, or mentor, you must have a clear mission and vision for working with Black males. Your guiding purpose (i.e., mission) and vision of what is necessary to achieve that purpose will guide you through the activities contained within this book. For example, the activities that relate to setting goals, inspiring college-bound dreams, developing character and personal attributes, and constructing a K-12 college-bound plan of classes, extracurricular activities, standardized test scores, and summer camps are driven by a mission and vision that moves beyond hopes of proficiency to dreams of empowerment.

The Life Skills & Core Values Vocabulary will assist in the development of your vision. Before beginning the task of working with Black males you must develop a vision of the type of men whom your efforts are designed to develop. Whether a classroom teacher or parent, a coach or mentor, or a counselor or principal, you must determine the type of values, life skills, and guiding principles that you would like to teach young men. You will discover that each school day provides opportunities to engage in discussions, suggest reading material, and teachable moments for helping young men to develop the critical-thinking skills through which to process their daily behaviors.

As a father, I find that each school day I engage in discussions with each of our sons in regards to such issues as character, integrity, responsibility, perseverance, compassion, tolerance, and respect. Whether I am talking to my sixteen-year-old about relationships with peers at his high school or my ten-year-old about being responsible in fulfilling his morning responsibilities in preparation for leaving for the school bus, each day is full of teachable moments. However, such moments can easily be squandered without a long-term vision of the type of men whom my wife and I envision our sons becoming.

The section on Multiple Intelligences will greatly enhance your efforts at assisting Black males in identifying their gifts, talents, abilities, and learning styles. This understanding can provide the springboard toward career dreams and aspirations which may not have previously been considered. As a result of the national pressure of raising standardized test scores and preparing students for end-of-grade exams it is possible to forget that first and foremost our responsibility is to teach, raise, and develop young people. If we can successfully inspire, inform, push, and prepare them to pursue their respective dreams and aspirations, surely proficiency levels is within reach. However, if we lift them to proficiency levels without developing their character, critical-thinking skills, and giving them ownership of their own futures we certainly will have missed the mark.

Overview: Key Points

1. Black males, despite socioeconomic, geographical, or cultural differences share cultural commonalities in the areas of academic achievement and social skill development.

2. Black males make up the largest group of low-performing students and represent a disproportionately higher rate of suspensions, expulsions, and special education placements.

3. White students take 200 percent more AP classes; have average SAT scores over 100 points higher (22 percent); and have average ACT scores 5 points higher (22 percent).

4. Home-school relationships must be driven by a common focus.

5. The unemployment rate for Blacks without a high school diploma is 30 percent, while the unemployment rate for Blacks with a college degree is 6 percent.

6. Increasing Black male achievement requires a collaborative effort between adult stakeholders throughout the school community.

7. Systemic, sustainable increases in student achievement are the result of a marathon which must allow frequent opportunities for students who get a slow start to catch up.

8. Thoughtful class placement and teacher assignment are essential to Black male academic success and positive social skill development.

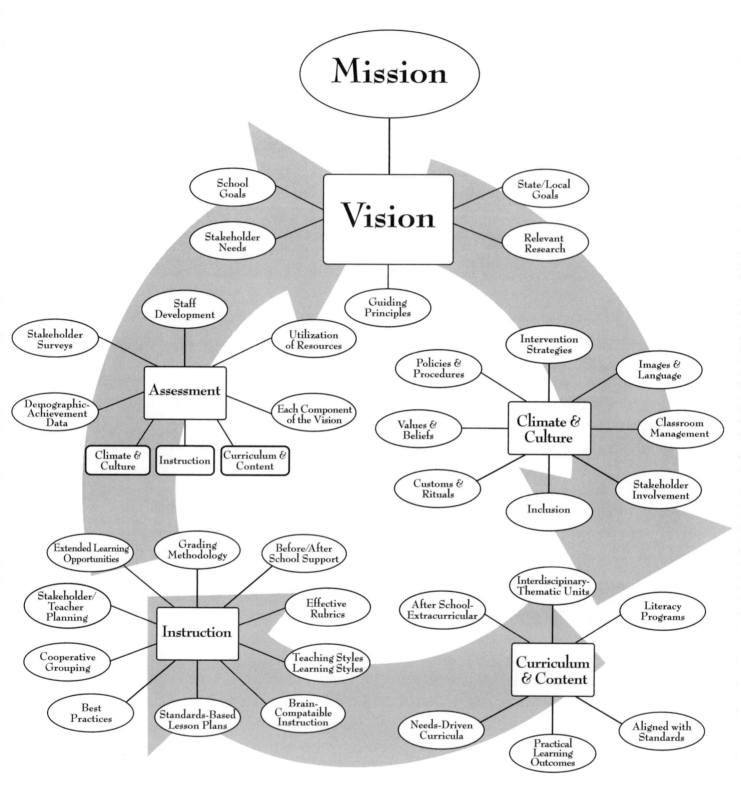

Illustration taken from, *Increasing Student Achievement: Volume I, Vision* (page 5)

According to the 2001 report for the National Center for Education Statistics, *Educational Achievement and Black-White Inequality:*

- *Black students, while representing only 17 percent of public school students, account for 32 percent of suspensions and 30 percent of expulsions. In 1999, 35 percent of all Black students in grades 7-12 had been suspended or expelled from school. The rate was 20 percent for Hispanics and 15 percent for Whites.*

- *Black children are labeled "mentally retarded" nearly 300 percent more than White children and only 8.4 percent of Black males are identified and enrolled in gifted and talented classes.*

- *Black males in their early 30s are twice as likely to have prison records (22 percent) than bachelor's degrees (12 percent).*

- *A Black male born in 1991 (today's 7th grade student) has a 29 percent chance of spending time in prison at some point in his life. The figure for Hispanic males is 16 percent, and for White males is 4 percent.*

- *A Black male is 700 percent more likely than a White male to be sentenced to a local, state, or federal prison.*[1]

- *Black males are imprisoned at a rate of 3,405 per 100,000 (3.4 percent); Hispanics at a rate of 1,231 per 100,000 (1.2 percent); and Whites at a rate of 465 per 100,000 (.465 percent).*[2]

- *17.5 percent of Black students, 13.2 percent of Hispanic students, and 9.3 percent of White students in grades K-12 were retained at least one grade.*[3]

- *13 percent of Blacks ages 16-24 have not earned a high school credential. The rate for Whites is 7 percent.*

- *30 percent of Black high school students have taken advanced mathematics courses compared to 45 percent of Whites.*

- *5 percent of Black high school students take a fourth year of a foreign language with 2 percent taking an AP foreign language course.*

- *12 percent of Black high school students take science classes as high as chemistry and physics.*

- *27 percent of Black high school students take advanced English.*

- *Black students take AP exams at a rate of 53 per 1,000 students. The rate for Hispanic students is 115 per 1,000 and for Whites is 185 per 1,000.*

- *The average SAT scores for Black students is 433V and 426M; for Whites it is over 22 percent higher at 529V and 531M.*

- *The average ACT score for Black students is 16.9; for Whites it is nearly 30 percent higher at 21.8.*

- *The unemployment rate for Blacks ages 16-19 is 25 percent.*

- *The unemployment rate for Blacks without a high school credential is 30 percent, 19 percent with high school but no college, 10 percent with some college but no degree, and 6 percent with a bachelor's degree.*

Chapter 1
Mission

Educators, activists, and assorted sages have given us scores of maxims that extol the value of education, but the most poignant words I have ever encountered on the necessity of education for African Americans were those of a Mississippi slave owner who in 1832 wrote: "Knowledge and slavery are incompatible." Indeed, they are. And thus, it is not difficult to understand why at one point in American history it was illegal to teach slaves to read and write. Just as the denial of education is a proven method of subjugating a people, there can be little doubt that access to education is potentially a definitive means to the self-enlightenment and self-realization of a people, which in turn spells liberation. By that I mean liberation from all the 'isms': racism, sexism, provincialism, and the individualism that prevents us from building sturdy Black bridges.

— Johnnetta B. Cole

Before forging ahead to identify problems, conceptualize solutions, or develop implementation plans, you must go through the painstaking task of clarifying your mission, i.e., purpose. Contemplating, conceptualizing, and clarifying your mission is a time-consuming, self-reflecting, gut-wrenching task. It requires, amid the chaos and confusion of raising and teaching children, you stop and reflect on whether you are doing the right thing, going in the right direction, or have any real understanding of the challenges, hopes, and dreams of the Black males whom you are raising, teaching, counseling, coaching, or mentoring. Without devoting the needed time to clarifying the mission, teachers are hired, the football season begins, schools open, programs are implemented, and subsequent failure is virtually guaranteed. This outcome does not necessarily mean people aren't working hard, the adult stakeholders in the school community don't care, or that groups of people aren't putting in a lot of time and energy into trying to help these young men. The problem is, we are so busy doing things, we never stop long enough to clarify what we want to accomplish, what types of men we want to develop, and where we ultimately want these young men to go as a result of all of the energy and effort we are devoting to them.

Chapter 1: Key Points

1. Without a clear mission, substantive, systemic, and long-term increases in student achievement levels for Black males is unlikely.

2. The mission exists on four distinct levels (district, school, department or program, and individual).

3. Each person must answer the questions:
   - "What is my role?"
   - "What levels of Black male achievement do I want to influence?"
   - "How committed will I be to the mission?"

4. All role players must identify their respective roles and work together to ensure student success.

5. The passion of the individual for the mission paves the way to fulfilling the institutional mission.

6. A goal for increasing Black male achievement must be driven by a mission explicitly focused on "Black male achievement" with the emphasis on the work ethic and acceptance of responsibility.

7. The statement, "I don't see color" hinders the development of strategies necessary to meet the unique needs of Black males and families because color is how we are defined and how we define ourselves. It is always a factor, explicit or implicit.

8. Begin with a focus on one child.

What is Your Role?

Having considered the information presented in this Chapter regarding the tremendous influence teachers, parents, coaches, counselors, administrators, mentors, and adults throughout the school community have in the lives of young men describe your primary role and the level of influence you want to have.

My primary role and the level of influence I want to have is:

_____

_____

_____

_____

_____

_____

_____

_____

_____

_____

_____

_____

_____

What is Your Mission?

Your mission represents your guiding purpose as it relates to teaching, parenting, coaching, or mentoring the young man whom you are focusing on. Is your overriding mission to build character and leadership skills, close the achievement gap, ensure he enrolls in honors, AP, or gifted classes, ensure he graduates from high school, or ensure he is prepared for, and enrolls in, college?

For example, as a classroom teacher, is it your mission to inspire the young man you are focusing on to discover and pursue his dreams? As a parent, is it your mission to guide him into the schools and classrooms which are most nurturing of his abilities and most reaffirming of his dreams? As a mentor, is it your mission to expose him to the broad range of career opportunities based on his unique talents, gifts, and abilities? Or, as a coach, is it your mission to develop his social, moral, physical, spiritual, and intellectual abilities so he may become a strong husband and father?

State your mission as it reflects your guiding purpose for your involvement within the life of this one young man.

My Mission is:

_____

_____

_____

_____

_____

_____

Coach Carter

1. Host a movie session with teachers, coaches, mentors, parents, and/or students.

2. Provide each attendee with a note pad and ask each person to make note of the following:

   - Does Coach Carter appear to have a clear sense of mission and if so, describe what it is?

   - Does Coach Carter appear to have a clear vision, and if so, describe what it is?

   - Identify two other characters and describe their sense of mission and vision.

   - Identify the collaborators and supporters of Coach Carter's vision.

   - Identify the anti-collaborators.

   - What would you identify as the three primary components or strategies Coach Carter used to get the players to buy in to his vision?

   - What would you identify as the key turning point of the attitude change of the players?

   - What would you identify as the key turning point of the attitude change of the school's principal?

   - Complete a 'Web of Protection' for Coach Carter's son and for one other player on the team.

3. How was Coach Carter able to achieve such a dramatic attitude change with his players without parental support, staff support, or peer support?

4. Why did his players want to succeed for him?

Illustration taken from, *Increasing Student Achievement: Volume I, Vision* (page 47)

Sample Adult Roles

Parent

- **Mission:** To raise a highly-educated, God-centered Black man able to pursue his God-given potential.

- **Vision:** To provide a nurturing faith-based environment, encouraging of academic achievement and driven by high expectations which continually reinforce a set of core values and guiding principles.

- **Strategies:** Church involvement, supportive and encouraging household and family culture, encouraging of relationships with positive male figures, active collaboration with school-based personnel, and continual reinforcement of and exposure to high academic expectations.

Teacher

- **Mission:** To develop an effective home-school collaboration to pave the way to achieving the highest academic and social skill development of Black male students.

- **Vision:** To provide a nurturing, principle-centered classroom, reinforced by strong teacher-parent (or other significant adult) communication, driven by brain-based and cultural–gender-specific instructional strategies, founded on classroom management strategies and grading methodology which are consistent with the mission.

- **Strategies:** Opening presentation to reinforce belief in student potential and academic expectations, reinforced by support materials and grading methodologies consistent with student needs, further supported by strong relationships with influential adults, and driven by clearly-defined research-based instructional strategies which meet the needs of learners.

Counselor

- **Mission:** To ensure that every Black male has a K-12 academic plan which will enable him to pursue postsecondary education.

- **Vision:** To ensure equitable representation of Black males in advanced, honors, and AP classes, in the National Honor Society, and on the school's honor role and that parents are fully-informed as to the options, opportunities, support programs, and courses of study available to their sons in grades kindergarten through 12.

- **Strategies:** An ongoing series of parent seminars, guest speakers, college fairs, career days, community partnerships, alumni mentoring, and providing parents with simple steps and continual advice to avoid the foreseeable pitfalls of Black male academic achievement.

Coach

- **Mission:** To provide an opportunity for Black males to develop the athletic skills and character to provide them with an opportunity to acquire a college education.

- **Vision:** To assist players in developing athletic skills, discipline, character, critical-thinking skills, and attitude to be successful on the field, in the classroom, and in their future life as men, husbands, fathers, and role models.

- **Strategies:** An indoctrination into a system of beliefs and expectations. A pairing of younger players with older players to reinforce the core values and guiding principles of the program. A meeting with parents, teachers, and community representatives to convey expectations, and ensure open lines of communications. Identify movies, books, and guest speakers to reinforce the program's values and beliefs.

Administrator

- **Mission:** To create a disciplined school environment which nurtures and cultivates high academic achievement and ensures equity of achievement and expectations among Black male students.

- **Vision:** To increase enrollment in honors, AP, and gifted classes, publicly celebrate Black male academic achievement, provide early identification of academic potential at the elementary and middle schools, and have academic expectations continually reinforced by staff persons and the surrounding community.

- **Strategies:** Gather and analyze class enrollment data, grade point averages, Black male participation in academic clubs, and reinforce academic achievement expectations at local churches, barber shops, parks and recreation athletic teams, and throughout the school community.

Mentor

- **Mission:** To encourage college matriculation and graduation among Black male students.

- **Vision:** To ensure that Black males understand what is needed to get into and graduate from college, are exposed to the wide range of career options and opportunities resulting from a college education, and develop the type of personal character and core values which will help them to make a positive contribution to their community.

- **Strategies:** Introduction to Black men and women who are college graduates, visits to college campuses, monitoring of their high school course schedules as they relate to postsecondary and career pursuits, and ensuring that they have the necessary academic, moral, and financial support for college admissions.

Note that within each of these respective missions, the focus on Black males is explicitly stated. The missions don't refer to, "an identifiable demographic group" or "all students." While there may certainly be other missions which relate to the overall school community, other demographic groups of students, and the success of the school's athletic teams, closing any achievement gaps and increasing Black male achievement require a specific mission, specific strategies, and an individual commitment to do so.

Student Role

"As your teacher, I am committed to your academic success. I have written my mission for teaching and my vision of the type of classroom environment needed to ensure the best environment for teaching and learning. However, ultimately, my role is to assist you in your success. You must have your own mission as how you will commit yourself to learning and a vision of the level of success which you want to achieve."

Teacher

- **Mission:** To develop an effective home-school collaboration to pave the way to achieving the highest academic and social skill development of students.

- **Vision:** To provide a nurturing, principle-centered classroom, reinforced by strong teacher-parent (or other significant adult) communication, driven by brain-based and cultural–gender-specific instructional strategies, founded on classroom management strategies and grading methodology consistent with the mission.

Parent

- **Mission:** To raise a highly-educated, God-centered Black man able to pursue his God-given potential.

- **Vision:** To provide a nurturing faith-based environment, encouraging of academic achievement and driven by high expectations which continually reinforce a set of core values and guiding principles.

1. Take a sheet of paper and at the top, write, "My Mission." What is your mission as it relates to academic achievement?

2. Take another sheet of paper and at the top, write, "My Vision." What is your vision of the level of academic achievement you will achieve?

Chapter 2
Vision

What Blacks are now being taught does not bring their minds into harmony with life as they must face it. When a Black student works his way through college by polishing shoes, he does not think of making a special study of the science underlying the production and distribution of leather and its products that he may some day figure in this sphere. The Black boy sent to college by a mechanic seldom dreams of learning mechanical engineering to build upon the foundation his father had laid, that in years to come he may figure as a contractor or consulting engineer.

— *Dr. Carter G. Woodson*

Taking the time to clarify your role, identifying the level of influence you want, and stating your mission must now be translated into a vision, i.e., what must be done to fulfill the mission. Conceptualizing a vision for your classroom, household, school, program, or church will require discussions with and input from the stakeholders who impact and influence the lives of the young men within your school community. To focus more specifically on ensuring the academic achievement and social skill development for the young man whom you have identified, your vision will determine the scope of the goals you set and the goals you encourage this young man to set for himself:

- Do you envision his reaching proficiency or becoming academically advanced?

- Do you envision his graduating from high school or graduating from college?

- Do you envision his escaping poverty or achieving financial prosperity?

- Do you envision his getting a job on the assembly line or being an executive in the ivory tower?

- Do you envision his becoming a talented athlete or a scholar athlete?

- Do you envision his enrolling in the Air Force or Military Academy or signing up at an Armed Forces recruiting office?

- Do you envision him discovering and pursuing his passions or getting a minimum wage job?

No matter how widely the visions vary between teachers and parents, administrators and mentors, counselors and coaches, or the school board and the school community, there must be a willingness to collaborate between the adult stakeholders before there is any real opportunity for anyone's vision to be realized.

- The teacher who envisions a young man reaching proficiency should support the efforts of a parent who envisions his scoring above the 90th percentile on standardized testing.

- The parent who envisions his or her son graduating from high school should support the efforts of a counselor who envisions his attending and graduating from college.

- The coach who envisions a player enrolling in basic classes to remain academically eligible should support the efforts of a parent who envisions her son enrolling in college prep classes.

- The principal who envisions meeting the school improvement goals of a 10 percent increase in reading scores should support the efforts of a teacher who envisions "Stand and Deliver Fridays" to motivate young men to read a book a week.

The vision my wife and I have for our sons has, in many cases, not been totally understood by friends, family, or by all of their teachers. We have been accused of pushing them too hard, having expectations which are unreachable, and holding them to standards which are unattainable. Fortunately, most of those who have not totally understood our passion, our purpose, or our expectations, have generally collaborated with and supported us in our efforts. However, be assured, the greater your vision for the success of Black males, the greater the number of people who will tell you it's unrealistic and who will actively undermine your efforts to achieve it!

Chapter 2: Key Points

1. The scope of your vision will define the scope of your strategies.

2. The school and home vision should be in alignment.

3. Your beliefs and your experiences define what you do.

4. Consider your vision for Black male enrollment in honors, academically gifted, and AP classes.

5. Determine the needed values to be taught and reinforced.

6. Black males should be held to the highest standards and expectations.

7. Lessons should reflect Black men who embody the core values and guiding principles you are teaching and reinforcing.

8. Learn and use a student's passions to lead him into learning.

9. Helping students to discover their dreams can help to place school into a meaningfully relevant context.

10. Consciously affirm and inspire higher aspirations, i.e., college, career, life.

11. Statistics show that students who take algebra I, geometry, and chemistry are more likely to go on to college.

12. Currently, only one out of three Black college students is male.

What is Your Vision?

Enough said, what is your vision for the young man whom you have identified? How will you utilize the tremendous opportunity you have to influence his emotional, social, and intellectual development in ways which will enable him to overcome the negative influences of peer pressure and media images? How will you inspire the highest academic achievement and affirm the highest educational attainment? Will you develop a vision of a life of hope and promise and be uncompromising in your demand for Standard English usage, social skill development, and developing his intellectual and critical-thinking skills?

If you are a mentor, coach, or pastor, how will you model the highest standards of manhood and communicate your uncompromising expectations of his promise and potential? What lessons will you teach when witnessing ill-mannered behavior, non-Standard English usage, or lack of respect and responsibility?

Your vision will determine your expectations and your expectations will determine your actions.

My Vision is:

_____

_____

_____

_____

_____

_____

_____

Life Skills & Core Values Vocabulary

Life Skills & Core Values
Vocabulary

Accountability. *To be accountable and to accept responsibility for ones conduct or actions.*

Choices. *The act, opportunity, power or privilege of choosing freely. To pursue an end or purpose which requires the exercise of judgment.*

Citizenship. *Performing the duties and responsibilities in accordance with the rights of a person recognized as a member (citizen) of a community or government.*

Collaboration. *To work together toward some common goal or objective.*

Commitment. *To accept responsibility and apply oneself to the successful completion of a task or action.*

Community Service. *To make a valuable contribution to uplifting, edifying or supporting the quality of life for others.*

Compassion. *To demonstrate human kindness toward the plight and needs of others.*

Consequences. *The resulting effect of one's choices or actions.*

Conscience. *The sense of moral goodness regarding one's own conduct, intentions or character, together with a feeling of obligation to do right or to be good; a sensitive regard for fairness or justice.*

Consciousness. *Marked by strong feelings, emotions, and thoughts. The state of mind indicated by a high level of mental awareness.*

Courage. *Firmness of mind and spirit in the face of great difficulty. The mental or moral strength to persevere in the face of opposition, danger, fear, or hardship. To stand firm for one's principles or beliefs despite criticism, difficulty, or opposition.*

Decision-making. *The act of engaging in careful and thoughtful consideration of choices and their related consequences before drawing a conclusion or engaging in actions.*

Determination. *To demonstrate firmness of purpose and to display personal resolve at completing a task or reaching a decision.*

Dignity. *To carry oneself with honor and respect.*

Diligence. *The steady, careful, and persistent effort that one devotes to his or her work, duties or responsibilities.*

Etiquette. *The conventional rules of social behavior and the customary behavior of members of a profession toward each other.*

Fairness. *To demonstrate a sense of justice that is impartial, free of favoritism or bias that is consistent with rules, logic, or ethics.*

Fortitude. *The ability to exhibit courage in the midst of great pain or adversity.*

Future Focus. *The act of developing a vision or gaining clarity for one's life or the achievement of personal goals.*

Honesty. *To demonstrate fairness, justice, and truthfulness in character and behavior.*

Independent Thinking. *Decisions that are not made under the control or through the undue influence of others.*

Initiative. *To demonstrate the ability to take action, begin a task, or create a plan on one's own accord without being directed by others.*

Integrity. *To adhere to a code of moral or artistic values. To demonstrate language and behaviors that are guided by honesty and the quality of incorruptibility.*

Intelligence. *The ability to apply knowledge to manipulate one's environment or think abstractly. And, the ability to learn, understand, or deal with new or trying situations.*

Justice. *To demonstrate the fundamental principle of moral rightness in attitude or actions. To uphold what is just and in accordance with honor, standards, or the law.*

Kindness. *To demonstrate affection, helpfulness, or sympathy toward others.*

Maintaining Health & Fitness. *The condition of being sound in body, mind or spirit. Consciously engaging in those activities and consuming those foods that contribute to an overall positive physical and mental state.*

Organization. To prepare an orderly structure that enhances one's opportunities to become successful and to effectively complete tasks.

Patience. To demonstrate the ability to endure hardship, perseverance or forbearance in one' demeanor or attitude.

Perseverance. A personal quality of remaining determined and steadfast in the pursuit of a worthy cause or goal in spite of obstacles or opposition.

Persistent. To refuse to give up or let go of one's goals and objectives. To obstinately endure despite challenges and obstacles.

Personal Development. To take responsibility for one's own growth, development, and expansion of knowledge.

Personal Pride. A sense of self-respect and personal satisfaction in one's self and one's actions.

Planning. To formulate a detailed series of steps or actions designed to accomplish a predetermined task or goal.

Preparation. To consciously engage in those mental and physical actions that place oneself into a state of readiness.

Promptness. To consciously be aware of schedules and appointments leading to preparing oneself to be punctual.

Reflection. The honest, inward focus and evaluation of one's actions, behaviors, and experiences.

Research. The systematic investigation and study or something directed at establishing facts and developing new conclusions.

Resilience. The ability to continue toward a goal or objective in spite of challenges, obstacles, misfortune or circumstances beyond one's control.

Respect. To demonstrate appreciation for, and consideration of others. To demonstrate conduct toward another that conveys a high sense of moral value or appreciation.

Responsibility. To accept accountability for one's conduct and actions. The ability to make moral or rational decisions and to be answerable for one's behavior.

Restraint. *To demonstrate the ability to intelligently and responsibly control one's actions.*

Setting Goals. *To consciously establish a focus on measurable achievement.*

Style. *A superior distinctive manner of writing, speaking or conducting one's duties and responsibilities.*

Survival. *To live through circumstances or consequences that may be outside on one's direct control or influence.*

Trustworthiness. *Actions and mannerisms that inspire the confidence of others in one's reliability. Deserving of the trust of others.*

Truthfulness. *Being sincere in actions, character, and what is being stated; a conscious attempt to honestly state or acknowledge the truth.*

Multiple
Intelligences

Performance Profile for Jalani Wynn
Iowa Tests of Basic Skills® (ITBS®)

Multiple Intelligences Theory

Bracing as it is to behold one's own array of intelligences, it is even more energizing if one can bring them to bear effectively at school, at home, at the work place, and in those regions of creative imagination which are so important to each of us.

— Howard Gardner

Dr. Howard Gardner developed the Theory of Multiple Intelligences, commonly referred to today as "M.I. Theory," while serving as a researcher at Harvard University in 1979. He and his colleagues were contracted by the Bernard Van Leer Foundation to investigate human potential. The Theory of Multiple Intelligences was published in Gardner's book, *Frames of Mind*. Gardner identified seven general areas of intelligence in his initial research findings, but stated that there may be more. He has since published an eighth area and identifies intelligence as not only doing well on a test or memorizing the fifty state capitals, but as solving a problem or creating a product that is valued in a culture.

'Solving a problem' encompasses computing two-digit multiplication, but it also includes forging a team, one capable of working collaboratively to accomplish a difficult task, from a group of individuals. 'Creating a product' includes turning clay into a bust, but it also means developing a new dance. And 'valued in a culture' means just what it implies: that others find merit in the work.

The educational applications of Multiple Intelligences Theory are far-reaching and have led to everything from expanded classroom lessons to the development of whole schools termed "Multiple Intelligences Schools."

While Multiple Intelligences Theory is widely recognized as the ways in which we acquire knowledge (learning-styles) and ways in which we apply what we know, it also is reflective of how we think, or more succinctly stated, "how we know." Each of us has experienced the sensation of "knowing." Whether it is empathy for the pain of a child, solving complex problems, humming a tune, choreographing a complex dance routine, performing a martial arts kata or painting a landscape, we just know.

In Maslow's Hierarchy of needs, he sights the highest level of human development as the level of self-actualization. The level of being or the level of knowing. This is the synergistic level which we seek to achieve in solving the many complex problems within a school community which hinder our efforts to lift students to their highest levels of achievement. Effective Multiple Intelligences grouping (teaming) can help us to achieve this self-actualizing level.

How We Learn:

As an example, some people may rely greatly on Visual/Spatial Intelligence to learn. Such individuals would learn best through slides, transparencies, graphic illustration, and other visual representations of what is being presented.

How We Apply What We Know:

Those same people may be highly Verbal/Linguistic in how they apply what they know. They may be very good at writing or speaking rather than being able to apply what they know through artist renderings or illustrations.

How We Think:

In yet another sense, the same individuals might be particularly proficient in problem solving, the conceptualization of complex processes, and in the sequencing of steps.

Thusly, they learn best through images (Visual/Spatial). They apply or communicate what they've learned best through writing or speaking (Verbal/Linguistic), and they create or "think" most effortlessly when solving problems or sequencing steps (Logical/Mathematical).

The complexities of M.I. Theory is that no two people utilize the same combination of intelligences in exactly the same way. Also, no two people are equally well developed in each of the intelligences. While some people solve complex scientific or mathematical problems very well, others have a better understanding of people, and still others demonstrate a higher intellectual understanding of art or music.

In a typical school community you will find:

- individuals who appear to effortlessly communicate with others (Interpersonal);

- individuals who perform well in subjects requiring complex problem-solving abilities like math and science (Logical/Mathematical);

- individuals who demonstrate an unique gift for drawing, illustrating, decorating, or designing things (Visual/Spatial);

- individuals who easily remember tones and melodies and appear to effortlessly catch on to raps, songs, and musical compositions (Musical/Rhythmic);

- individuals who are fascinated with the outdoors and appear to have a particular connection with the outdoors, plants, and animals (Naturalist);

- individuals who have highly-developed hand-eye coordination and are highly-skilled in sports, dance, gymnastics, or building complex models (Bodily/Kinesthetic); and

- individuals who have a passion for writing poetry, short stories, storytelling, debating, or discussing issues (Verbal/Linguistic).

My experience is that every classroom is comprised of students with varied and unique intellectual gifts. While these intellectual gifts may not always reveal themselves on tests, quizzes, or traditional academic assignments, they are there nevertheless. Developing an understanding of multiple intelligences and helping students to discover their unique intellectual gifts will help to cultivate a classroom where children learn to value their gifts, and the diversity of gifts represented by their classmates.

Multiple Intelligences Theory provides a framework for understanding human potential. For helping children to identify the varied and diverse career options available to them where they can engage in work which provides the opportunity to apply their unique intellectual gifts.

All children can be inspired to spread their wings and soar toward their dreams.

How to Get Started

There are two approaches to Multiple Intelligences grouping: "Like Grouping" and "Cross Grouping." While each has its merits, "Like Grouping" is more effective and should be done first. The problem-solving discussions within such groups move quickly and effectively and the groups, as a rule, tend to be highly effective.

Benefits of "Like Grouping" are:

- faster problem-solving;

- group members appear to *hear* each other better;

- fewer disagreements and less need to explain;

- problem-solving efforts are often driven by personal passion;

- intellectual capacity and contributions of all group members are validated and appreciated;

- group accepts ownership of planning and implementation;

- natural cultural and gender diverse grouping occurs;

- cross-generational, cross-gender, and cross-cultural relationships are developed;

- a heightened sense of ownership of operational and implementation strategies; and

- personal empowerment of group members.

Note:

>*Cross grouping should never precede Like Grouping. While Like Grouping validates individual intelligence if cross grouping precedes this intellectual validation long-held stereotypes and beliefs can contribute to the group being counterproductive. For example, in our schools we have historically valued Verbal/Linguistic and*

Logical/Mathematical intelligence above all else.

Students highly developed in the arts are considered "talented," but not intelligent, as Ronald Stone notes in his book, *Creative Visualization*:

Western dependence on reason has meant that we frown on such things as the imagination. Schooling develops reasoning powers and implicitly, if not explicitly, treats the imagination as unimportant. It is not surprising, therefore, that children very soon give up being imaginative. As this process continues the growing person finds it more and more difficult to form mental images, simply because this particular faculty goes unused.

Students who are highly proficient in dance and sports (Bodily/Kinesthetic) are referred to as having "natural talent" and abilities, and again, are often considered less intelligent than those demonstrating talents and abilities in language arts, math, and science (typically the core curriculum).

David Lazear, in his book, *Seven Ways of Knowing: Teaching for and with Multiple Intelligences*, notes the intellectual foundation of Bodily/Kinesthetic intelligence:

Current brain research has revealed that bodily/kinesthetic capacities comprise a complex, intricate, highly integrated network of brain/body operations. The motor cortex of the brain executes specific muscular movements, with the right side of the brain controlling the left side of the body and the left side of the brain controlling the right side of the body. The cerebral cortex acts as a perceptual feedback mechanism, which both feeds information to the spinal cord and receives input from the rest of the body through the spinal cord. Once information has been sent and/or received and interpreted, the motor cortex brings about the appropriate body responses to match the information received by the cerebral cortex.

Once a culture has been established in which group members value and validate the multiplicity of intelligences, and thusly, the intellectual contribution of all group members, there can be benefits to "Cross Grouping."

- Individual group members are recognized as experts within their uniquely highly-developed intellectual domain and are deferred to leading the discussions pertinent to their domain.

- The group discussion is directed toward holistic strategic plans.

- Ideas are quickly discussed and solutions are holistically conceptualized leading to a framework for the smaller focus group discussions.

- Individual group members can carry the large group discussions back to a smaller more focused group for carrying out action plans.

Review the outline of each of the Multiple Intelligences domains on the following pages. Read all eight domains before attempting to establish your personal priority. Re-read each of the eight domains and indicate the priority for the three categories:

1. How I best learn.

2. How I best apply what I've learned.

3. How I best solve problems.

Help your students to identify their strongest and weakest intelligences. Provide frequent opportunities for students to showcase their intellectual strengths and to strengthen their weak areas.

Verbal/Linguistic Intelligence (Language)

Word Smart. The ability to think in words. Responsible for the production of language and all the complex possibilities that follow, including: poetry, humor, storytelling, abstract reasoning, and the written word.

People who demonstrate this intelligence tend to appreciate the subtleties of grammar and meaning. They may spell easily and enjoy word games. They understand puns, jokes, and riddles and have developed their auditory skills. They tend to memorize words and phrases easily and demonstrate an interest in the sound and rhythm of language.

This includes such categories as:

- *Poetry*

- *Humor*

- *Storytelling*

- *Abstract reasoning*

- *Writing*

People highly developed in this intelligence usually demonstrate abilities or interests in:

- *the capacity to use language, demonstrated in the form of oral and written communication;*

- *proficiency at acquiring information from reading, writing, talking, and debating; and*

- *a passion for things like poetry, humor, storytelling, debating, and creative writing.*

Logical/Mathematical Intelligence (Processes)

Process Smart. The ability to calculate, quantify, and carry out complex mathematical operations. Associated with what is called "scientific thinking." Deductive/inductive thinking/reasoning, numbers and recognition of abstract patterns.

People who demonstrate this intelligence tend to be logical in their thought processes, calculate well, and tend to be precise and methodical. They demonstrate the ability to move from the concrete to the abstract and enjoy computer games and puzzles. They tend to think conceptually and explore patterns and relationships. They organize their thoughts well and do well in applying a systematic approach during problem solving.

Typical of this intelligence is:

- *a highly-developed ability to figure things out and identify patterns; and*

- *a highly-developed ability to analyze and solve complex problems, particularly in subjects like math and science.*

People highly developed in this intelligence usually demonstrate:

- *great problem-solving capacity;*

- *proficiency with numbers and complex equations;*

- *proficiency at applying the scientific method to everyday problems, even relationships; and*

- *proficiency at sequencing steps and understanding complex patterns.*

Interpersonal Intelligence (People and Relationships)

People Smart. Ability to understand others and their feelings. Ability to work cooperatively in a group as well as the ability to communicate, verbally and non-verbally with other people.

People who demonstrate this intelligence tend to display empathy for and understanding of others. It also involves the ability to effectively communicate, verbally and non-verbally, with other people, and is often demonstrated through the ability to assume leadership roles.

Typical of this intelligences is:

- *the capacity to make distinctions in the feelings, intentions, and motivations of others;*

- *the ability to "read" people and interact effectively based on those cues;*

- *the capacity to make friends easily and function well on group projects and within group settings;*

- *the ability to share opinions and empathize with the opinions and feelings of others;*

- *a desire to work on group projects and within group activities;*

- *the ability to effectively mediate conflicts and cooperate with others;*

- *the ability to understand and recognize stereotypes and prejudices;*

- *an interest in volunteering to work with others; and*

- *the ability to offer constructive and appropriate feedback.*

Intrapersonal Intelligence (Introspective, Spirit/Pride)

Self Smart. Knowledge of the internal aspects of self, including the ability to plan and direct one's life. The ability to understand such areas as inner feelings, spirituality, range of emotional responses, self-reflection, and sense of intuition.

This intelligence allows us to be conscious of our self-identify and wholeness. According to Gardner, this intelligence is the most private and requires all other intelligence forms to express itself, such as language, music, art, dance, symbols, and interpersonal communication, often providing a sixth sense into the "spirit" of others. People highly developed in this intelligence tend to have a good sense of their strengths and weaknesses. Their metacognition, their thinking about their thinking, is especially refined.

Typical of this intelligence is:

- *being in touch with one's feelings and demonstrating an inner sense of self;*

- *demonstrating highly develop intuition regarding institutional or individual spirit, i.e., morale;*

- *having a strong focus on dreams and aspirations or future possibilities; and*

- *being proficient at concentrating, focusing, and inner reflection.*

People highly developed in this intelligence usually demonstrate abilities or interests in:

- *pursuing personal interests;*

- *understanding their own strengths and weaknesses;*

- *being or working alone;*

- *empathizing with the feelings and emotions of others;*

- *developing a strong sense of self, and oftentimes do not defined themselves by group parameters; and*

- *demonstrate a highly-developed ability for introspection and self reflection.*

Visual/Spatial Intelligence (Images)

Picture Smart. The capacity to think in three-dimensional terms. Ability to create internal mental pictures. Deals with such things as the visual arts, navigation, map-making, interior/fashion design, and architecture.

This intellectual domain is mostly located in the right hemisphere of the brain in what is known as the "parietal lobes." This intellectual domain is utilized in our ability to find our way around a given location, including being able to get from one place to another. People who demonstrate this intelligence enjoy maps and charts, like to draw, build, design, and create things, think in three-dimensional terms, love videos and photos, enjoy color and design, enjoy pattern and geometry in math, and may like to doodle.

This includes such areas as:
- *graphic and visual arts,*
- *design and illustration,*
- *the ability to coordinate colors and patterns,*
- *photography,*
- *navigation,*
- *map making, and*
- *architecture.*

People highly developed in this intelligence usually demonstrate abilities or interests in:
- *fashion or interior design;*
- *animation, illustration or fine art;*
- *multi-dimensional thought patterns;*
- *organizing information visually;*
- *having a good sense of direction;*
- *doodling, painting, sculpting, drawing and other arts and crafts activities;*
- *mazes, puzzles, hidden picture activities, awareness; and*
- *visually sequencing events and forming mental images.*

Bodily/Kinesthetic Intelligence (Movement)

Body Smart. The ability to manipulate objects and fine-tune physical skills. Ability to use the body to express emotion as in dance, karate, gymnastics, body language, and sports. The ability to learn by doing.

People who demonstrate this intelligence tend to be coordinated and agile. They tend to demonstrate good hand-eye coordination, balance, timing and equilibrium. Their gross or fine motor skills may also be well developed. They tend to be hands-on learners and demonstrate the ability to learn by doing.

People highly developed in this intelligence usually demonstrate highly-developed abilities in such areas as:

- *sports,*
- *martial arts,*
- *dance,*
- *gymnastics,*
- *rock climbing,*
- *water/snow skiing and surfing,*
- *roller skating and bicycle riding,*
- *weight lifting,*
- *boxing,*
- *carpentry,*
- *building things,*
- *sculpture, and*
- *surgery.*

Musical/Rhythmic Intelligence (Music)

Music Smart. Sensitivity to pitch, melody, and rhythm including such capacities as the recognition and use of rhythmic and tonal patterns, sensitivity to sounds such as the human voice and musical instruments.

People who demonstrate this intelligence tend to remember melodies well, enjoy listening to music, are able to keep a beat, make up their own songs, notice background and environmental sounds, and differentiate pattern in sounds.

This intelligence is demonstrated in such ways as:

- *creating and directing musical compositions;*

- *singing and playing musical instruments; and*

- *showing proficiency at remembering melodies, tunes, songs, or instrumental patterns.*

Naturalist Intelligence (Environment)

Environment smart. The ability to recognize plants, animals, and other parts of the natural environment, like cloud patterns or rocks formations. Heightened understanding of animal behaviors and the natural environment, such as the African jungle, Amazon Rain Forest, or urban jungle of New York City.

People who demonstrate this intelligence tend to have a heightened sense of being connected to their environment and the world around them. They demonstrate a heightened sense of awareness in such areas as camping, hiking, fishing, animal behaviors or relating to the natural environment.

Typical of this intelligence is:

- *the ability to understand and interact well with animals;*

- *the ability to interact well in the natural environment; and*

- *a highly-developed ability in landscaping, gardening, hiking, and outdoor activities.*

People highly developed in this intelligence usually demonstrate abilities or interests in:

- *outdoor work and activities,*

- *working with animals,*

- *working with landscape design, gardening, or farming, and*

- *nature walks, bird watching, butterfly watching, changes in weather patterns, and cloud formations.*

Follow Your Dreams

To further the discussions regarding college-bound dreams, have students read the book, *Follow Your Dreams: Lessons That I Learned in School*. Teachers may also choose to read the book to students during home room, in advisory periods, or during class time designated for reading and literacy activities. Mentors and coaches can also provide the books for mentees and players.

Use the story to stimulate discussions of such topics as:

- Overcoming obstacles

- How negative peer pressure can hinder you from pursuing your dreams

- How following the negative example of friends can hinder a person from pursuing his own dreams

- How low expectations can hinder a person from putting forth their best effort and keep them from affirming their dreams

- How a person's circumstances such as living in poverty, being in foster care, or being adopted can contribute to their making excuses

- Why it is important to have dreams as a means of setting goals

- Why setting academic goals are important and how to avoid setting goals which don't reflect a person's true potential

- How to identify your unique gifts, talents, abilities, and interests as a means of discovering your dreams

- Why affirming and visualizing your dreams can help you to meet people and find out about programs which can support you in pursuing your dreams

- Why the author believes a college education is important for his children and should be part of every student's dreams

Develop A College-Bound Vision

Some of the steps to developing a college-bound vision for your home, school, classroom, church, or community program are:

1. Ask all the teachers, coaches, parents, and mentors in your school or program to bring in items representing their alma mater (i.e., pennant flags, T-shirts, caps, sweatshirts, gym shorts, bumper stickers).

2. Ask each adult and student to contact 5 colleges and request their catalog and view book.

3. Ask local business owners to contribute college items from their alma mater.

4. Contact all the colleges within your state for catalogs, posters, and view books.

5. Devote a bulletin board or wall and identify the admission requirements for your state's colleges and universities. Create an HBCU wall.

6. Identify alumni from your school who have graduated from college and assign students to write up their biographies.

7. Take all the information you have gathered and decorate a wall under the heading "Do You Have College-Bound Dreams?"

8. List the alma maters of your school's staff, parents, grandparents, mentors, and community residents.

9. Have adults within your school community constantly asking, "Where are you going to college?"

10. Get copies of the books, *A Middle School Plan for Students with College-Bound Dreams* and *A High School Plan for Students with College-Bound Dreams*.

11. Develop college clubs for students who are committed to a particular college and plan field trips, research projects, E-mail chats, and discussions with admissions officers and alumni.

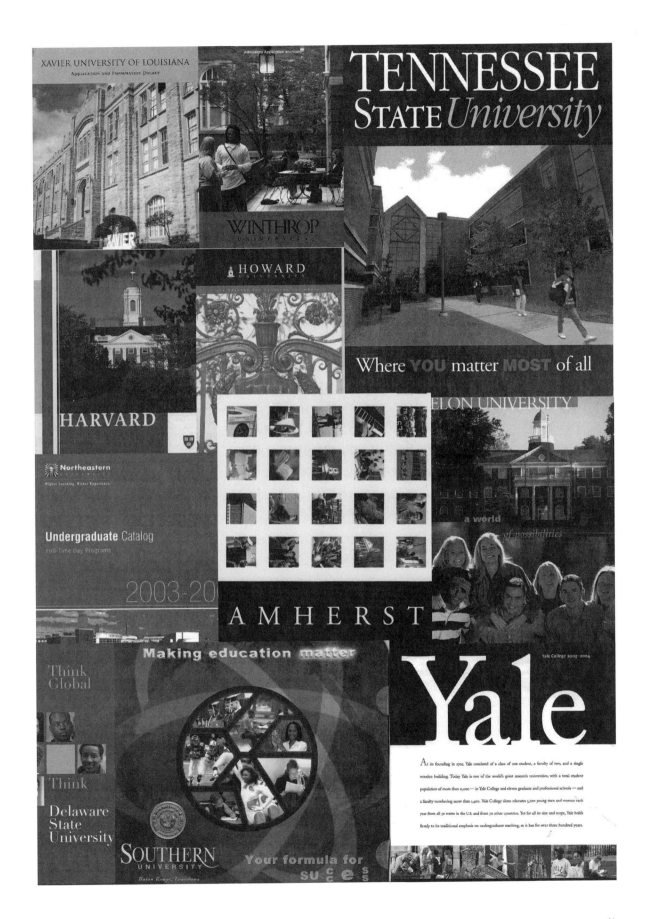

Business or Index Cards

The purpose of this activity is to encourage young men to prepare themselves for applying for jobs and/or college admissions by setting personal achievement goals. As young men engage in identifying career aspirations, areas of interests, and personal accomplishments they elevate their consciousness of the importance of setting goals and preparing a business card of one's achievements. Some young men, as in the case of the examples, may already have stellar academic performance, while other young men may have more artistic, athletic, and/or community service accomplishments. The activity should help young men to identify their strengths and become more conscious of potential areas of weakness. The activity can also be used to affirm goals or future accomplishments, i.e., "What I would like my business card to look like in the future."

Take a sheet of paper and list the following:

A. Current grade point average
B. Year of high school graduation
C. SAT/ACT scores (for high school students)
D. Sports
E. Hobbies, interests, clubs
F. Honors, AP, or academically gifted classes
G. Best Quality
H. College choices
I. College major
J. Current grade in school

"At some point in your life you will either have to apply for a job or submit a college application. A prospective employer or a college admissions officer will review your grades, test scores, and personal achievements in assessing whether to hire you or to admit you into their college or university. Some people will be satisfied with their current level of achievement, while others will want to set higher goals. Whatever the case, your current information lets you assess where you are. You have to decide if this is where you want to be or if you want to set higher goals.

Here are some sample business cards of young men in various grade levels with various levels of personal and academic achievements."

Class of 2007 • Current Grade: 10 • GPA: 3.125

Hobbies/Interests: Varsity Football [Linebacker]; Gospel Choir; Advanced Honors Choir; 21st Century Leaders; music; basketball; swimming; reading; building/repairing musical instruments; and acting

Special Talents/Abilities: Selected to Fulton County Honors Choir [Fall 2004]; Selected to Georgia All-State Honors Choir [2001]

North Springs High School
7447 Roswell Road
Atlanta, GA 30328

Sophomore
Performing Arts Magnet Program

CJ Moore

Music Producer
Football Coach

Class of 2006 • Current Grade: 11 • GPA: 3.3 • 10th Grade: SAT: 560V - 570M ACT: 25

Honors/AP Classes: H 10th Gr Lit; H 11th Gr Lit; H Algebra II; H Pre-Calculus; H Physics; H Biochemistry; H Organic Chemistry; H Economics; H Spanish Culture; AP Computer Science; AP Studio Art; AP Spanish; AP US History.

Hobbies/Interests: Varsity Football [Linebacker]; Varsity Lacrosse [Midfielder]; Varsity Track & Field [400, 200, 4x100, 4x400]; Spanish Club; Urban Arts Club; Martial Arts [Black Belt]

Special Talents/Abilities: Working knowledge of the following computer software: Microsoft Word; QuarkXPress; InDesign; Adobe Photoshop; Adobe Illustrator; Adobe Elements

Work/Volunteer Experience: Tri-lingual ESOL tutor; Martial Arts Instructor; Youth Basketball Coach; Knights of Pythagous; Math, Science, and Spanish tutor.

North Springs High School
7447 Roswell Road
Atlanta, GA 30328

Junior
Visual Arts • Math/Science Magnet Program

Visual Arts • Graphic Design

Mychal-David Wynn

Class of 2012 • Current Grade: 5 • GPA: 4.0

Hobbies/Interests: Football [Defensive End, Running Back]; Lacrosse; Track & Field [Shot Put, Javelin, Discus]; Basketball [Guard, Forward]; Martial Arts [Blue Belt]; Acting; Chess Club; Youth Usher,

Awards:
1995 Baby Race Champion
2003 1st Place County Shot Put
2003 2nd Place AAU Jr. Olympics Shot Put
2005 Best Defensive Player

Camps/Programs: Amherst College Football Camp; NSHS Football Camp

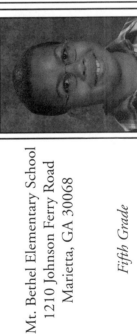

Mt. Bethel Elementary School
1210 Johnson Ferry Road
Marietta, GA 30068

Fifth Grade

Actor • Sports Medicine

Jalani Wynn

As parents, the vision for a son begins before the child is born into the world. In many African societies there is a formal naming ceremony where a name is chosen to represent the vision of the family for the child. The name of our firstborn is Mychal-David Isiah Wynn. Mychal signifies firstborn, named after his father. David is taken from the Holy Scriptures signifying, to become king. Isiah represents the name of his grandfather on his mother's side, taken from the Holy Scriptures, signifying one who is called of God. Mychal-David Isiah Wynn is the firstborn, called of God who is to become king. The name of our second born is Jalani Malik Wynn. Jalani is taken from the Swahili language, signifying mighty. Malik is taken from the Arabic language, signifying master. Jalani Malik Wynn is to become a mighty master within the Wynn legacy.

Our vision for our sons is that they will honor God, bring honor to their family, become highly-developed intellectually, have strong character, be spiritually-focused, physically strong, and become independently successful men who will honor their wives and be an example to their children. We are also preparing our sons to pursue their dreams and to discover their purpose so they will be examples of the hope and promise of Black men. What we do as parents is all directed toward this end.

A Parent's Vision

As a parent, what is your vision for your family? While parents generally want the best for their children, sometimes the challenges of parenting and the stress of raising children can distract parents from focusing on the future of their family, and particularly, the future of their children.

Consider:

- How often you say, "I Love You."

- How often you affirm your child's intelligence, talents, and gifts.

- How often you make reference as to your child's potential and future.

Read "A Parent's Vision" on the following page and write your vision for your son and/or your family.

A Parent's Vision

My vision for our household is that everyone will enjoy the freedom to openly and honestly express his or her feelings, emotions, ideas, and opinions as long as it is done in a respectful and concerned manner and does not hurt or offend others. As a family we will work to provide a safe, loving, caring, and supportive environment. We will encourage each other in developing and pursuing our individual and collective dreams.

Each member of our family will have a role to play and a responsibility to fulfill in supporting the individual and collective vision of the family.

As your parent(s) I/we must do our best to provide a positive model, through our example, of those personal qualities and characteristics that are consistent with achieving our vision; such character traits as diligence, determination, commitment, responsibility, and dependability. We must also demonstrate guidance, leadership, and support through praising those behaviors and actions that are expected and through disciplining those behaviors and actions which are unacceptable and considered detrimental to achieving the highest possible level of individual and/or collective success and prosperity.

As children, we expect you to recognize your role within the family and your responsibility to the world around you. Personal qualities such as honor, compassion, courage, and integrity cannot be given nor taken away, but will help you to become a person to be admired and respected by others. In more ways than we can count, the world is crying out for people who will make a difference in societal issues, the environment, justice, peace, and moral leadership. Our vision is that each of us will in some way make a difference.

What I Won't Do for My Friends

1. I won't steal for my friends.

2. I won't cheat for my friends.

3. I won't act dumb for my friends.

4. I won't do drugs for my friends.

5. I won't disrupt the class for my friends.

6. I won't disrespect, laugh at or ridicule others for my friends.

7. I won't intentionally fail for my friends.

8. I won't behave irresponsibly for my friends.

9. I won't knowingly hurt others for my friends.

10. I won't destroy my life or anyone else's for my friends.

    Anyone who would ask me to do any of these things, is not my friend.

Written by Mychal Wynn © Rising Sun Publishing, Inc.

Chapter 3

Climate & Culture

Walk into any racially mixed high school cafeteria at lunch time and you will instantly notice that in the sea of adolescent faces, there is an identifiable group of Black students sitting together. Conversely, it could be pointed out that there are many groups of White students sitting together as well, though people rarely comment about that. The question on the tip of everyone's tongue is 'Why are the Black kids sitting together?' Principals want to know, teachers want to know, White students want to know, the Black students who aren't sitting at the table want to know ...Why do Black youths, in particular, think about themselves in terms of race? Because that is how the rest of the world thinks of them.

— *Beverly Daniel Tatum*

Understanding the unique issues (i.e., media images, peer pressures, societal perceptions, cultural icons) influencing the attitudes and behaviors of Black males is paramount to developing effective communication, intervention, and empowerment strategies. Perhaps there is no group of students who are more misunderstood than Black students. Teachers and parents are perplexed and exasperated as they openly question:

"Do they value academic achievement?"

"Why do they have such a negative attitude toward school?"

"Do they aspire toward anything other than sports and entertainment?"

"Why do their parents allow them to leave home with their pants hanging down at their knees?"

"Why are they so angry and why are they so confrontational?"

"Why does my son always leave his homework at home? If not for all of the zeros he would be an 'A' student. He just doesn't care."

Chapter 3: Key Points

1. Black males need compassion to understand the unique issues confronting them, followed by strategies in response to those issues.

2. Zeros and F's aren't a proven intrinsic motivator and should be reconsidered in lieu of strategies which inspire the necessary effort and levels of learning.

3. Frequent opportunities for young men to increase their grade by demonstrating gradual, systemic increased levels of learning better prepares them for standardized testing and end-of-course exams.

4. An understanding of Multiple Intelligences helps to develop holistic strategies which builds relationships and conceptualizes effective processes.

5. Building relationships with parents helps to ensure consistent expectations and a focus on meeting student needs.

6. Visiting a student's home can help you learn the hopes and dreams of his family.

7. Seek to understand the attitudes and perceptions of Black males toward the school community.

8. Understand the rap and hip-hop influences which impact the beliefs and aspirations of Black students.

9. 'The Dozens,' 'The Showdown,' and inappropriate language have histories in Black culture and are predictable behaviors requiring proactive strategies.

10. Do not compromise in teaching 'Standard English.'

11. Gather data and honestly assess school and classroom culture regularly.

12. Teach young men how to work together through frequent use of teaming.

What Do I Really Know?

1. Take a sheet of paper and divide it into four parts by folding lengthwise and cross ways or by simply drawing one line across the middle of the page and one line down the middle of the page.

2. Label each of the four areas:

    a. Role Models: i.e., athletes, entertainers, teachers, parents, coaches, or pastors.

    b. Family Environment: e.g., father at home, brothers and sisters, relative incarcerated, educated, impoverished, transient, or stable.

    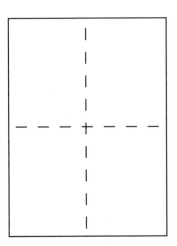

    c. Cultural Characteristics: i.e., culturally reflective style of walk, dress, language, speech, values, and beliefs.

    d. Personal Characteristics: e.g., self-esteem, peer influence, leadership skills, or artistic talent.

3. Complete each of the areas by writing down everything you know about the young man whom you identified in Chapter one. After completing each of these four areas of influence, turn the sheet of paper over and write down his goals, dreams, and aspirations.

4. Rather than making broad stereotypes, review the cultural-, societal-, social-, family-, and community-influences on the following pages, checking those which have a significant influence in the life of your young man of focus.

Teachers and parents alike discover how little they know about their sons and students and just how great the cultural, gender, and generational divide is between today's young people and their parents and teachers. This is, in large part, because we fail to talk with and listen to young people. Any socioeconomic differences between teachers and families only magnifies the cultural, gender, and generational gaps.

Personality Type

☐ Extravert   **or**   ☐ Introvert
☐ Sensitive   **or**   ☐ Intuitive
☐ Thinking   **or**   ☐ Feeling
☐ Judging   **or**   ☐ Perceiving

Multiple Intelligences

☐ Verbal/Linguistic
☐ Logical/Mathematical
☐ Visual/Spatial
☐ Bodily/Kinesthetic
☐ Musical/Rhythmic
☐ Interpersonal
☐ Intrapersonal
☐ Naturalist

Learning Style

☐ Global
☐ Analytic
☐ Auditory
☐ Kinesthetic
☐ Tactile
☐ Visual

Refer to the book, *Ten Steps to Helping Your Child Succeed in School* for a complete description of personality types, multiple intelligences, and learning-styles

---

Home

☐ Single-parent
☐ Multi-generational (i.e., grandparents, parent, siblings with children)
☐ Unorganized or dysfunctional
☐ Has assumed role of man of the house
☐ Lacks goal setting and/or long-term focus
☐ Lacks positive parental support
☐ Unbalanced or nutritionally deficient diet
☐ Substandard housing or homeless
☐ Lack adequate medical and dental care
☐ Transient or itinerant family

- ☐ Lack academic support
- ☐ Siblings in multiple school settings (i.e., elementary, middle, and high school)
- ☐ Non-assertive or inarticulate parents
- ☐ Illiterate or marginally-literate family
- ☐ Few or no college graduates in immediate family
- ☐ Lack academic support
- ☐ Family or family members living in poverty or on welfare
- ☐ Under or unemployed parents
- ☐ Parents who feel powerless to address school-related issues
- ☐ Teenage pregnancies
- ☐ Family history of physical and/or substance abuse

Community

- ☐ High stress community
- ☐ Negative interactions with law enforcement
- ☐ Lacks cultural alternatives
- ☐ Lacks esthetic values
- ☐ First-hand experience with violent crime
- ☐ Lacks positive male role models
- ☐ Lacks youth development, support programs and activities
- ☐ Lacks effective school-community partnership

Gender-specific

- ☐ Physically mature
- ☐ Emotionally immature
- ☐ Socially immature
- ☐ Difficulty maintaining focus in the classroom
- ☐ Challenges female authority
- ☐ Lacks physically accessible positive male role models
- ☐ Culturally distinctive style of walk ("The Walk")
- ☐ Culturally distinctive handshake
- ☐ Verbally and physically aggressive
- ☐ Short attention span

Values, Beliefs, Peer Group

- ☐ Values athleticism over academics
- ☐ Highly influenced by peer pressure
- ☐ Lacks positive peer support
- ☐ Role models are people who are recognized by peers, portrayed on mass media through television and radio
- ☐ Low academic motivation
- ☐ Associates a sense of self-worth with clothing, shoes, jewelry, and hair styles
- ☐ Relatives or friends in jail or on parole
- ☐ Uses profanity and/or inappropriate language
- ☐ Exhibits uncooperative behavior
- ☐ Culturally distinctive speech ("Black English")
- ☐ Relies upon and demonstrates nonverbal communication (e.g., hands, eyes, body language)
- ☐ Affinity toward team and group activities
- ☐ Rebellion against 'whiteness'
- ☐ Highly influenced by current pop culture (music, tattoos, hair styles, dress, attitudes toward authority, jewelry)

If you perform this exercise with two Black males from the same household, raised by the same parents, taught the same values, and held to a similar set of expectations, you are likely to find both cultural commonalities and differences. In addition to the cultural differences, you are likely to find differences in multiple intelligences, personality types, learning-styles, values, and beliefs. To truly understand Black males, you must identify and examine as many influencing factors as you can.

What I Think & Who I Am

Answer each of the following and then have students do the same. Have a classroom discussion to compare your answers to theirs and to compare their answers to each other.

- ❑ Favorite foods
- ❑ Favorite clothes, designers
- ❑ Favorite cars
- ❑ Favorite sports
- ❑ Favorite athletes
- ❑ Favorite entertainers
- ❑ Favorite entrepreneurs
- ❑ Favorite teachers
- ❑ Favorite politicians
- ❑ Favorite music
- ❑ Favorite dances
- ❑ Favorite songs
- ❑ Time you go to bed
- ❑ Time you wake up
- ❑ What you eat before going to school
- ❑ What you do after school
- ❑ What you do on the weekends
- ❑ Drive to school or take school bus
- ❑ Hero
- ❑ Heroine
- ❑ Role Model
- ❑ Planning to go to junior college
- ❑ Planning to go to four-year college or university
- ❑ Planning to attend HBCU
- ❑ Planning to get an athletic scholarship
- ❑ Planning to get an academic scholarship
- ❑ Planning to get a creative scholarship, i.e., music, dance, art, theater

Who We Are?

Family and Community:

Describe your family. Who lives in your home (e.g., father, mother, brother, sister, nieces, nephews, or grandparents)? How would you describe your house (e.g., quiet, noisy, busy, big, or small)? How would you describe your neighborhood?

Describe what happens on a typical school day. What do you eat in the morning before you come to school? How do you get to school? How far do you have to travel?

Who We Are:

What types of things do you like to do? For example, what type of games do you like to play? What type of music do you like to listen to? What are your favorite clothes, shoes, or clothing styles (e.g., hip-hop, Sean John, Phat Farm, FUBU, NBA jerseys, or NFL jerseys)? What are your favorite dances? Do you have a favorite hair style? Do you have a special way or walking or talking? Do you have a tattoo and if so what does it mean?

What We Like:

Describe yourself. How do you feel about you? What are your special talents, gifts, or abilities? What are your hobbies, interests, sports, or favorite activities? How do you feel about your family? Who do you most admire in your family? How do you feel about your neighborhood? If you could choose to live someplace else where would it be? What do you do best? What do you have the most difficulty with? Do you make your own decisions or do you tend to go along with everyone else? What is your most attractive physical attribute? If you could change anything about yourself what would it be?

Remember, there are no good or bad, right or wrong answers.

Listen to What They Think

1. Have the young man, or group of young men, complete a one-page paper (e.g., narrative, rap, poem, autobiography) for each of the following:

    - What I want to be

    - What it means to be a man

    - What it means to be a father

    - People whom I most want to be like

    - My heroes, heroines, and role models

2. This activity can also be written onto note cards and used as prompts for a classroom or one-on-one discussion. When using the activity to stimulate a classroom discussion you must ensure that you cultivate an environment free of ridicule, put-downs, mocking, and name-calling to encourage the open and candid sharing of feelings, thoughts, ideas, and opinions. If you aren't able to do this, then it is best to focus on a one-on-one discussion.

Today, we're going to spend some time talking about ourselves. There aren't any right or wrong answers, we're going to talk about things at home and at school. We're going to try to describe things and people in our communities and the type of things we like to do.

First, let's talk about heroes, heroines, and role models. Role models are people who you most admire or would most like to be like. They could be people who you've seen on TV or people who live in your community. They could be people who own businesses or work in your community. They could be people in your family or even your friends.

Who Do You See?

1. Give a student a blank, unlined sheet of paper.

2. Direct the student to draw a large box onto the sheet of paper which will represent a mirror.

3. Ask the student to describe what and who he sees in his reflection.

4. Take a sheet of paper and write down what you see in the student.

What the young man sees in himself will direct his actions and behaviors, so too, will what you see in him. To encourage a young man who is a non-reader to affirm college is to have the highest expectations of your capacity and of his potential. When we look at young Black males who are at the bottom of the academic achievement gap, we rarely see the same level of academic potential as we do when the same young man walks onto a football field or a basketball court. Yet, there is so much evidence to support high expectations and high aspirations for young Black males.

Their legacy includes the greatest athletes, doctors, lawyers, educators, scholars, political leaders, statesmen, businessmen, scientist, inventors, aviators, adventurers, artists, mathematicians, architects, fashion designers, poets, musicians, novelists, and orators in the history of mankind. This is not fiction, this is fact.

The greatest challenge to implementing the ideas and strategies is your own expectations. In essence, who you see in the mirror.

Read What They Write

1. Engage a young men in a writing activity about such areas as:

    •   Favorite foods, clothes, cars, sports, entertainers, politicians, businessmen, entrepreneurs, recording artists, role models, dances, songs, places to live, teachers, and careers.

    •   Have him describe in detail a typical school day, i.e., what time he gets up, what he eats for breakfast, household responsibilities, before school routines, the school day, after-school activities, and after-school routines.

    •   Identify the things he is most interested in or most enjoys doing, e.g., basketball, martial arts, recording music, dancing, watching TV, playing video games, and participating in computer chat rooms.

2. Keep the papers and revisit this activity after you have had an opportunity to work through other activities and discuss the young man's dreams and aspirations. If this activity is performed during the beginning of the school year, a good time to revisit it would be nearing the end of the school year.

3. Compare what you learn through this exercise with what you thought you knew in the exercise, "What Do I Really Know?"

4. Another approach to this activity is to provide a young man with poster board, magazines, newspapers, glue, scissors, and markers. Ask him to make a poster of his dreams with pictures and words reflecting his interests, dreams, and aspirations.

The Dozens

1. Find out who is best at playing 'The Dozens' and challenge him to a duel; but there's a new twist. The challenge is to say the most positive, encouraging, uplifting, supportive, and edifying things.

    Start the game and get other young men involved. Encourage boisterous instigation of a positive nature. Notice the intensity, passion, and spirit or young men as they join in.

2. Discuss the history of "The Dozens." Discuss the tradition in ancient Africa. Describe the type of things you think young men in the village may have said about each other's fathers as a rite of passage into manhood.

3. Have each young man write "The Dozens" about himself. Have him proclaim his greatness, the cultural achievements of his people, a royal heritage, and future successes.

4. Have each young man write an essay about some of the negative language Black people use to describe themselves and each other. Have them develop a vocabulary list of words generally perceived to have negative meanings, e.g., bad meaning good and phat meaning nice, which they use to reflect positive feelings.

5. Play a game where each person makes a positive one-line statement about the person next to him.

6. Discuss the power words have on how a person feels about himself and, when used to uplift or encourage others can have in helping others to feel good about themselves.

7. Have each young man close his eyes and go around the room with each person making a positive one-line statement about themselves.

What Manner of Men Are We ...

1. Gather a group of young men, ideally eight to ten.

2. The poem, *What Manner of Men Are We ...*, may be photocopied for use in this exercise. Distribute a copy to each young man highlighting from one to three consecutive lines on each copy (i.e., the first young man has the first three lines highlighted, the next young man has the next two lines, and so on).

3. After you've highlighted all the lines in the poem, work with this group to prepare an oral recitation as follows:

    a. Let the young men recite their lines without any coaching. (Usually, they will hold their heads down, tap their feet, put their hands in their pockets, slouch as they stand, and are barely audible in their presentation.)

    b. Recite the poem for them. (This is where you have to use expression in your voice. Place emphasis on certain words; inject anger into such words as "in the boxing rings"; inject pain into such words as "castration and degradation.") Have them repeat each line, then each stanza, eventually reciting the entire poem with inflection.

    c. Now have them repeat the poem. (See if someone steps forward with some clarity and authority. When that person does, respond "Yes, that's it, put some power into it!") Remember, young men gravitate toward team sports and competitive group activities. Helping one person to "slam dunk their recitation" will inspire others, and eventually the entire group, to follow.

4. After you've repeated this poem several times, you should begin to witness the following:

    a. Their competitive nature begins to show as they try to become louder, more forceful and more emotional.

    b. Someone will ask, "Can I do his part?"

    c. When several people have done well and someone makes a mistake, they will begin to exert peer pressure. (Be sure to keep this positively focused.)

    d.   Someone will step forward and say, "I know it all. Can I do the whole thing?"

5. As you continue to coach them, encourage them to step forward when it's their turn. Encourage them to raise their voices; inject some emotion; move their arms using meaningful gestures; and dramatically express themselves (harness their passion).

6. Encourage them to establish eye contact with you while they're reciting their parts.

- With continued practice and encouragement, you will begin to see:
    - They will develop increased self-pride and self-confidence.
    - They will begin to articulate words they've never articulated or may have avoided before.
    - They will look forward to taking center stage.
    - They will want to do more poems and presentations.

What Manner of Men Are We …

What manner of men are we
      who move gracefully and swiftly
      along the football fields and basketball courts of the world
Constantly pounding or being pounded
      in the boxing rings of Atlantic City and the inner city
Robbed from the bosom of Mother Africa
      and the richness of South Africa
Having journeyed form the mountain top to the selling block
Experiencing over 300 years of
      castration and degradation,
      every indignity and humiliation
Yet continuing to grow tall and strong
Creating a history rich in achievement
We discovered blood plasma and the cotton gin
      gas masks and harpoons, baby carriages and traffic lights
      machines to plant seeds and machines to stretch shoes
We were the first to die
      in the struggle for this country's independence
      and the first to successfully perform open heart surgery
We are Martin and Marcus, Malcolm and Benjamin
      Frederick and W.E.B., Jesse and Booker T.
We are Jesse, Jackie, and Joe
      the Big E, and the Big O
We are Clyde the Glide and Earl the Pearl
We are the Watusi and the Mandingo
There are none bigger, none better
      none taller, and none stronger
When we have it all together
That's what manner of men we are!
                  — Mychal Wynn

Preparing for the Inevitable

Write down how you would respond to the following:

Greg Jones who is likely to receive a failing grade comes to class again without his homework:

_____

_____

Wayne Miller has gotten bored and is clowning in class again:

_____

_____

Mychal-David Wynn is staring at you. This is a showdown:

_____

_____

_____

Jalani Wynn just hit Louis Jones:

_____

_____

Alphonso Carreker just used profanity:

_____

_____

_____

Following are some ideas and alternative responses to situations such as these:

"Dr. Jones, I know inside of you are seeds of brilliance. I'm trying as hard as I can to help them to find fertile ground. You see Dr. Jones, homework is one of the means I use to help those seeds find fertile ground. Homework is an important part of fertilizing the soil for those brilliant seeds to sprout and take root. You know Dr. Jones, your homework is so important to bringing forth the brilliance within you, I'm going to give you a special opportunity to stay after class and discuss it with me."

"Mr. Miller, please accept my apologies. I haven't given you an opportunity to participate in the discussion. What is your opinion on this?"

Acknowledge Mr. Wynn's need for attention by positioning yourself near him during the next discussion. During the discussion, place your hand on Mr. Wynn's shoulder and bring him into the discussion.

"Mr. Wynn, what is your opinion on this?"

Acknowledge the ensuing conflict between Mr. Wynn and Mr. Jones by raising your voice to express your authority and intervention:

"Just a moment class, it appears Mr. Wynn and Mr. Jones have a conflict which could not have been resolved diplomatically. Mr. Wynn has just expressed his disapproval by attempting to inflict great bodily harm upon Mr. Jones."

You can further discuss how this conflict is in opposition to the class' code of conduct and the long-term ramification of a suspension.

While you are talking, Mr. Wynn and Mr. Jones have an opportunity to calm down. The class is now focusing on this behavior which they have identified as being unacceptable. The concepts of mutual respect and character development can be discussed through the leadership you've displayed by taking control of the situation.

"Mr. Carreker, we have already discussed the inappropriateness of certain language. You will have to write a one page paper as to why it is inappropriate and have your parent sign it."

What Do You See in Your Life?

1. Begin to set goals for and to visualize extraordinary achievement (e.g., straight A's, outstanding oratorical recitations, great musical and dance performances, clear, strong, and articulate expressions of thoughts and ideas, or varsity letter).

2. Make the following questions part of a routine dialogue with your students of sons:

    a. What do you want to be?

    b. Begin to affirm this regularly by saying such things as; "You have the power to become the greatest _____ ever." "What are you going to do when you become a(n) _____?"

    c. Close your eyes and see yourself there.

    d. Now tell me what you see?

    e. What did you learn in school today which will help you get there?

    f. Great! Such skills and information will help you to become a great ...

3. Have young men regularly read books about their goals and share or report on what they've read.

4. Get them in the habit of discussing their thoughts, ideas, and opinions.

5. Introduce young men to books about great Black men who have achieved the things they want to achieve and discuss with them how their lives compare with the lives of those men.

6. Ask them to visualize the success which these men experienced.

7. Identify positive quotations and poems which will help them to visualize and affirm their goals. Display these throughout your home or classroom (e.g., on the refrigerator, in the bathroom, his bedroom, walls) and periodically ask young men to recite them.

What Do You Pledge to Be?

Set aside some quiet time in the morning at school and in the evening at home. Have your young man close his eyes and focus on his goals. Encourage him to see himself achieving his goals and feel himself standing in victory.

Parents should have their son(s) include their goals in their nightly prayers. Parents should also join their son(s) in prayer in affirming their goals. Help them to visualize overcoming the obstacles and challenges in their lives.

1. Close your eyes.

2. Focus on your ultimate goal.

3. See yourself there, feel the success, and taste he victory.

4. Focus on one of the smaller goals; one of the things you must do today to move one step closer to your goal.

5. See yourself accomplishing this smaller goal.

6. Reinforce this exercise by gathering books, magazines, newspaper articles, films, and videos which provide visual images of his goals.

7. Repeat the affirmation on the following page.

A Pledge to Myself

Today I pledge to be
   the best possible me
No matter how good I am
   I know that I can become better

Today I pledge to build
   on the work of yesterday
Which will lead me
   into the rewards of tomorrow

Today I pledge to feed
   my mind: knowledge
   my body: strength, and
   my spirit: faith

Today I pledge to reach
   new goals
   new challenges, and
   new horizons

Today I pledge to listen
   to the beat of my drummer
Who leads me onward
   in search of dreams

Today I pledge believe in me

— Mychal Wynn

Discipline

The following rules are designed to establish the foundation of discipline:

1. "We are going to establish the rules for our classroom or club."

2. "We are going to identify a consequence for violating each rule."

3. "When I make a request and there's no immediate response, allowing the benefit of the doubt, I will repeat myself only to ensure that you heard me and that you understood my instructions."

4. "If there is no response, or if the response is slow and lazy, the consequences will be enforced."

Seeds of greatness ...

We are descendents of kings and queens, farmers, and artisans, politicians and teachers, generals and warriors. We must display the highest character, integrity, and intelligence befitting one of royal heritage. We must maintain a certain standard of behavior and code of conduct.

The history of the Black man in America is one in which we have often been stripped of our dignity, self-respect, honor, and humanity. We were brought into this country as chattel. We were not respected as human beings, but treated as property. The slave masters were not concerned with our feelings. They had no respect for our opinions. They had no compassion for our dreams and aspirations. They did everything conceivable to remove the Black man as the head of the household and destroy our family structure.

Understanding this history, we cannot establish discipline within young men without encouraging and building self-respect, integrity, honor, and responsibility.

Code of Conduct

1. Write down your classroom or home code of conduct. Develop these through discussions with your young men. Decide upon appropriate forms of discipline. Post the Code of Conduct, together with the agreed upon discipline, on a bulletin board, refrigerator, or a place where it can be visually referred to. You will discover peer pressure working for you to enforce the conduct which the class has determined appropriate. Mutual respect is developed as a result of your commitment to enforce what the class has accepted.

2. Incorporate into you teaching, and/or parenting style, firm, yet loving ways to communicate desired behavior. Never allow deviations from the code of conduct to go unnoticed. This may mean simply walking around the room and placing your hand on someone's shoulder without allowing them to interrupt the lesson.

3. Avoid confronting young men unless you're prepared to enforce your authority. Be careful not to make them lose face among their peers, always allow them the opportunity to retain their dignity and the respect of their peer group.

4. Here is a list of things to discuss in your classroom and/or home:

   - acceptable dress code
   - acceptable posture
   - acceptable personal hygiene
   - appropriate speech
   - appropriate manners
   - appropriate hand shake
   - personal pride
   -. dignity
   - character
   - kindness
   - love for self
   - love for each other
   - relationship to the world community
   - achieving respect without violence

- leading by example
- respect for self and others
- social problems and solutions

Discuss these ideas and issues within the context of the philosophical writings and teachings of Black men whom young men respect and admire. Look for opportunities to introduce them to historical figures and for opportunities for them to discuss popular current figures. In this way you help them to develop and articulate their own philosophies.

5. Expand this list to incorporate the unique problems and situations in your school or home. As you develop, discuss, and identify the acceptable behavior in your classroom and/or home, do so with the focus on the young men achieving their goals and pursuing their dreams.

6. Demonstrate to them that there is a correlation between their behavior and:
    - goal achievement;
    - social advancement; and
    - success in their lives.

7. Build the foundation of acceptable behavior upon the cornerstone of pride in themselves, responsibility to their community, their family, future children, future wife, and of their developing a personal quest for excellence. Laughing, giggling, negative words, and any other signs of discouragement must not be tolerated. Work toward bonding with young men and help them to bond with each other.

8. Discuss their ideas and help them to formulate their opinions about personal responsibilities. Talk about how Black men are portrayed in the media and what obstacles confront them in education and careers. Discuss how their attitude and character will affect how they respond to the challenges and obstacles confronting them.

Our Code of Conduct

1. We will begin each day by affirming our individual and collective greatness.

2. We will begin each day by giving each other a hug (or handshake).

3. We will always do our best to help each other achieve their goals and dreams.

4. We will always strive for the highest character, integrity, and honesty.

5. We will always maintain a passion for excellence in what we do. Anything worth doing is worth doing well!

6. We will always maintain the manners and posture worthy of a royal heritage, carrying ourself with pride and dignity.

7. We will always demonstrate respect for ourselves and for the rights and property of others.

8. We will never say negative or discouraging things to each other.

9. We will never hit, bite, kick or scream at each other.

10. We will apply each of the first nine codes of conduct as though someone was always watching.

A Man Is ...

A man is not quick to anger

    He's not one who's quick to brawl

If you see a man bullying others

    He's not a man at all

A man is not a quitter

    He's not one to turn and run

When the going gets rough, he gets tough

    He'll remain 'til the job is done

A man takes no satisfaction

    in seeing another fail

He encourages all to try

    and to believe that they can prevail

A man will never boast or brag

    or kick sand in your eye

He'll stand firm on his conviction

    with his head held to the sky

A man will always lend a hand

    when he finds a friend in need

His character and his integrity

    makes him a true friend indeed

                 — Mychal Wynn

Are You An Eagle or a Chicken?

Read the story, *"The Eagles who Thought They were Chickens."*

The questions are taken from Activity 5 of *"The Eagles who Thought They were Chickens Student Activity Book."*

How does the story relate to your school?

Think about the story and in what ways the characters and their behavior resemble the behavior of people in your school. For example the chickens who talk about the baby eagles, the roosters who beat the captured eagle, the Captain who destroys the lives of the people whom he captures, and the great eagle who knows who he is, where he comes from, and what his special gifts are.

1. Reflect for a moment on a typical day at your school. Describe the behaviors of people at your school and how they remind you of the behaviors of the characters in the story.

2. Reflect for a moment on a typical school day. Describe the behaviors of your family, friends, or classmates and how they remind you of the behaviors of the characters in the story.

3. If someone raised his or her hand to answer a question in class and got the answer wrong, describe how you think those who behave like chickens would likely respond.

4. Describe how your family, friends, or classmates would respond if you shared the following goals:

- A goal of attending college
- A goal of getting straight A's
- A goal of making the school's Honor Roll
- A goal of not talking about or putting down anyone
- A goal of becoming President

5. There are many similarities between the attitudes and behaviors of the characters in the story and our family, friends, and classmates. We are likely to know people who encourage us like the great eagle and people who talk about us and put us down like the chickens.

6. Write your own story about life in your school, home, on your athletic team, and/or in your community.

Lessons Learned

"Class, at the beginning of each week we are going to announce the word for the week. This word will be one of the words we will all affirm to breathe life-giving power into the seeds of brilliance which lie within each of us."

"This week's word is perseverance. Perseverance means to remain steadfast. To continue working toward your goals despite the obstacles and setbacks confronting you."

"Can anyone give me an example of how they have displayed perseverance in their lives?"

Other words to be introduced:

Diligence	Determination	Dedication
Fortitude	Character	Courage
Conviction	Compassion	Integrity
Wisdom	Understanding	Brilliance
Incredible	Fantastic	Wonderful

We can empower young men by identifying and affirming their special gifts. This may require changing our attitudes and perceptions. In the story about "Lying Lewis" most teachers saw Lewis as a lying and conniving young man who couldn't be trusted and had to be watched! However, Dr. Kuykendall saw a special gift with extraordinary potential. If we are to stop the seemingly endless flow of young men dropping out of schools and dropping into drugs and gangs, we must begin to affirm a better life for them. We must look for their gifts, help them see their own gifts, and nurture their extraordinary potential.

Despite prejudice and racism, ignorance and bigotry, there are doors of opportunities which we can empower them to open. Each day we should affirm with them such positive affirmations as the adaptation of the poem, "Born to Win."

Born to Win

I was born to become an Eagle

to spread my wings and fly

With strength and perseverance

I'll continue reaching toward the sky

I was born to become a Lion

to stand tall, proud, and free

My faith and determination

casting a light for all to see

And like a Ram I'll stand on the mountain top

greeting the dawn of each new day

Prepared to meet whatever obstacles

that should dare to block my way

I will stand before the rising Sun

with a sense of pride that stands the test

Accepting challenges, I will dare to dream

I will dare to become the best

— Mychal Wynn

Values

"Following is a list of values or personal attributes which we have discussed and which you have included in your vocabulary list. Write down a situation in which you have demonstrated the value, character trait, or personal attribute."

- ☐ Diligence

- ☐ Determination

- ☐ Perseverance

- ☐ Fortitude

- ☐ Integrity

- ☐ Honesty

- ☐ Compassion

- ☐ Sincerity

- ☐ Dedication

- ☐ Commitment

- ☐ Confidence

- ☐ Persistence

- ☐ Friendship

- ☐ Courage

- ☐ Conviction

- ☐ Respect for the rights and opinions of others

Responsibilities

"At the beginning of each week I am going to list the names of students and the responsibilities which I would like for them to accept for the week."

Classroom Responsibilities

Write down the name of a young man, the responsibilities you are going to assign, and the character traits the responsibilities are intended to develop.

Mark Young, collect homework.

Personal responsibility, communication skills, and leadership skills.

Mychal-David Wynn, daily quote from an African-American writer.

Oral skills, introduce to male role models, expand knowledge of Black history.

School Responsibilities

Shoes properly tied, shirt tails in pants, no caps.

Personal responsibility, dress code, self-respect, and dignity.

Shake hands when introducing self, establish eye contact, and speak in a clear, audible voice.

Self-confidence, self-esteem, self-pride.

Home Responsibilities

List of daily chores and household responsibilities (i.e., before school, after school, before bed).

Personal responsibility, personal hygiene.

Accepting Responsibility

"In our lives we must accept responsibility for what we do. Particularly those things which we do while exercising our own free will. Although others may encourage us to behave in inappropriate ways, we must accept responsibility for what we choose to do.

Before we act, we must consider the possible positive and negative consequences of our actions.

For example, if someone drinks and drives what are the positive and negative consequences which could happen as a result of their actions?

Following are some questions or situations which I would like for you to write a one paragraph response to. Explain the potential positive and/or negative outcomes."

Having sex

Joining a gang

Selling drugs

Taking drugs

Stealing a car

Robbing a bank

Graduating from high school

Graduating from college

Not taking school seriously

Dropping out of school

Having a baby before you establish a career

Getting so angry that you could kill someone

Teacher, Parent, & Mentor Workbook

Chapter 4
Curriculum & Content

Kunta Kente was the product of a society that held its young in high esteem and developed a network of role models and functional institutions to assist him in his social development. Until the day he was attacked and kidnaped by slavers, Kunta Kente had been raised in a fashion that clearly defined who he was, his responsibility to his parents, relatives, and community, and his sense of manhood.

— Useni Eugene Perkins

The area of curriculum and content encompasses such hotly debated issues as:

- Whether or not to formally recognize 'Ebonics' as a curriculum component.

- The infusion of Afrocentric thought into an otherwise Eurocentric curriculum.

- Ensuring that diverse cultures and viewpoints rise to the level of critical-thinking and classroom discussion.

- Addressing the gender, racial, religious, and cultural stereotypes in literature and social sciences.

- Whether or not students are introduced to the needed levels of scientific and mathematical thinking to compete globally.

- Whether or not there is too little, too much, or just enough content being covered during the school year.

- Whether or not there is sufficient alignment between what is taught in the classroom and what is tested on standardized, grade-level proficiency, end-of-grade, or high school exit tests.

Chapter 4: Key Points

1. The negative influences of peer pressure and popular culture must be countered through positive imagery of present and historical Black males infused into the curriculum.

2. The negative influences of peer pressure and popular culture is further reduced through the 'web of protection' created by a variety of adults and organizations.

3. Parents should consciously limit their son's access to negative media images.

4. Teachers should engage Black males in critical-thinking discussions of current events and pop culture influences.

5. Adults should be proactive in influencing peer culture directly and indirectly influencing peers themselves.

6. Teachers should identify opportunities for culturally-relevant research papers and lessons.

7. Black males should be encouraged and supported in honors, academically gifted, and AP classes.

8. There is a direct link between lack of literacy and criminal incarceration.

9. An elementary–middle–high school collaboration is needed to provide early intervention and early identification of academically-gifted Black males.

10. Infuse values into lesson design and program expectations.

11. Identify supplemental programs and activities to reinforce values and personal attributes.

12. Design lessons around student's dreams and aspirations to develop their critical-thinking skills and to construct their kindergarten-through-college plan.

Constructing a Web of Protection

1. Write down the name of a young man on each of the Circles of Influence and Web of Protection illustrations.

2. Review the completed Circles of Influence and identify the primary influences in the life of the young man within each of the circles.

3. Circle those influences which you would consider negative.

4. Using the blank, 'Circles of Influences' write the names of individuals or programs within each of the circles which currently provide a positive influence within the life of this young man.

5. Perform the following tally based on the individuals and programs you identified:

    Immediate Family Members: _____
    Relatives: _____
    Extended Family Members: _____
    Friends: _____
    Teachers: _____
    Coaches: _____
    Administrators: _____
    School Staff: _____
    Peers: _____
    Mentors: _____
    Programs: _____
    School Activities: _____
    Clergy: _____
    Other: _____

6. Review the sample 'Web of Protection' for Mychal-David Wynn.

7. Using the blank 'Web of Protection' attempt to identify those individuals and/or programs which could be used to provide a web of protection to counter-balance the negative influences which you identified on the 'Circles of Influence.'

Circles of Influence

Societal Influences

- Sexually Explicit Programming
- Promotes Violence as a Means of Problem-Solving
- Frequent Portrayal of Black Families and Professionals as Dysfunctional
- Lack of Positive Black Images
- Desensitizes Death and Handgun Violence
- Negative Role Models
- Glorifies, Profanity, Sarcasm, Sex, and Crime
- High Amount of TV Viewing
- Glorifies Athletic/Entertainment over Academic Achievement
- Holds Teachers in Low Regard
- Glorifies Fame, Fortune, and Infidelity
- Perpetuates Gender/Race Biases and Stereotypes

Home/Community

- Lack Adequate Study Time/Location
- Lack of Parental Involvement in Academic Tasks
- Lack of Positive Mentoring
- Lack of Self-Control/Self-Discipline
- Requires Before/After-School Care
- Underemployed or Unstable Household
- Limited Exposure to Successful Adults
- Lack Financial Resources
- Extended Family/Foster Care
- Single-Parent Households or Lack of Positive Male/Female Influence
- Low Household Goals/Lack of Planning
- Lack Academic Reinforcement
- Lack of Spiritual Foundation
- Negative Peer Pressure
- Negative Peer Values
- Many Teenage Pregnancies
- Negative View of Women
- Verbally/Physically Aggressive
- Uses Violence to Resolve Conflicts
- Negative Experiences with Law Enforcement
- Firsthand Experience with Abuse
- Victim or Perpetrator of Violent Crime
- Lack of Medical/Dental Care
- Poor Diet
- Limited English or non-English Speaking Households
- Community/Household Void of Inspiration and Positive Images
- Unorganized Households
- Illiterate or Marginally Literate Family

School

- Low Teacher Expectations
- Frequent Referrals/Suspensions
- Low Attendance
- Frequent Tardies
- Verbal/Physical Confrontations
- Lack of Respect for School Property
- Incomplete or Unfinished Homework
- Negative Teacher Attitudes Toward Students
- High Percentage of Free/Reduced Lunch
- Low Teacher Morale
- Frequent Classroom Disruptions
- Students Disruptive in Large Groups
- Students Frequently Unprepared
- Transient Student Population
- Lack Adequate Supplies and Materials

Individual

- History of Discipline Problems and Low Academic Achievement
- Lack of Respect for Individuals and Authority
- Negative Verbal/NonVerbal Communication
- Low Self-Esteem
- Lacks Positive Focus/Direction
- Uses Violence as a Means of Problem Solving
- Violent Outbursts
- Apathy
- Exhibits Self-Destructive Behaviors
- Few Long-Term Goals
- Lacks a Middle/Upper Class Mentor
- Lacks Nutrition
- Poor Grooming & Personal Hygiene
- Unrealistic Expectations
- Lacks Meaningful Relationship with a Caring Adult
- Does Not "Connect" Content to Outcomes

© Mychal Wynn • Rising Sun Publishing, Inc. (800) 524-2813

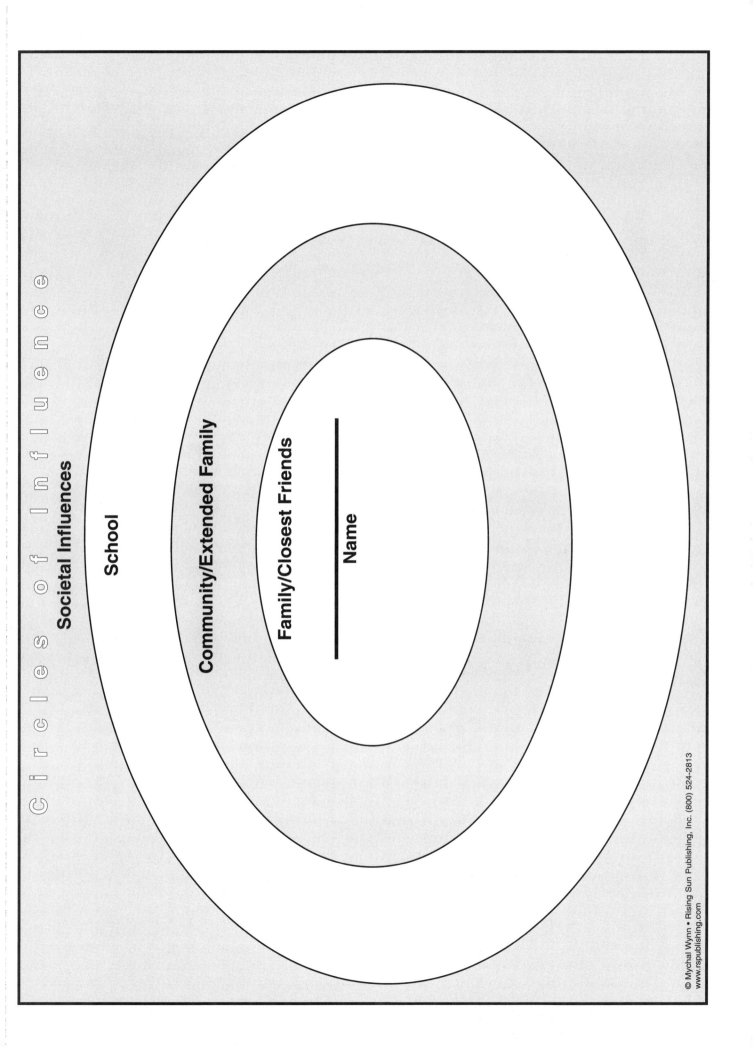

Circles of Influence

Societal Influences

School

Community/Extended Family

Family/Closest Friends

Name

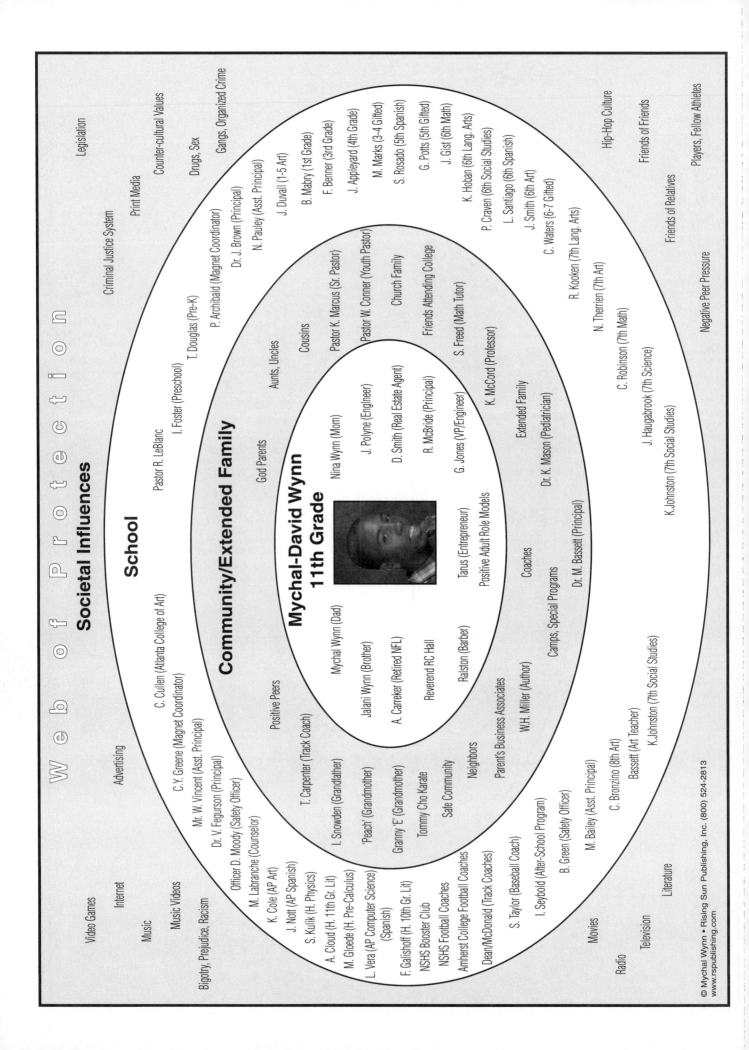

Web of Protection

Societal Influences

School

Community/Extended Family

Mychal-David Wynn
11th Grade

Legislation

Counter-cultural Values

Drugs, Sex

Gangs, Organized Crime

Print Media

Criminal Justice System

Hip-Hop Culture

Friends of Friends

Players, Fellow Athletes

Friends of Relatives

Negative Peer Pressure

Advertising

Internet

Video Games

Music

Music Videos

Bigotry, Prejudice, Racism

Movies

Radio

Television

Literature

P. Archibald (Magnet Coordinator)

Dr. J. Brown (Principal)

N. Pauley (Asst. Principal)

J. Duvall (1-5 Art)

B. Mabry (1st Grade)

F. Benner (3rd Grade)

J. Appleyard (4th Grade)

M. Marks (3-4 Gifted)

S. Rosado (5th Spanish)

G. Potts (5th Gifted)

J. Gist (6th Math)

K. Hoban (6th Lang. Arts)

P. Craven (6th Social Studies)

L. Santiago (6th Spanish)

J. Smith (6th Art)

C. Waters (6-7 Gifted)

R. Kooken (7th Lang. Arts)

N. Therrien (7th Art)

C. Robinson (7th Math)

J. Haugabrook (7th Science)

K.Johnston (7th Social Studies)

T. Douglas (Pre-K)

I. Foster (Preschool)

Pastor R. LeBlanc

C. Cullen (Atlanta College of Art)

C.Y. Greene (Magnet Coordinator)

Mr. W. Vincent (Asst. Principal)

Dr. V. Fegurson (Principal)

Officer D. Moody (Safety Officer)

M. Labranche (Counselor)

K. Cole (AP Art)

J. Nott (AP Spanish)

S. Kulik (H. Physics)

A. Cloud (H. 11th Gr. Lit)

M. Gloede (H. Pre-Calculus)

L. Vera (AP Computer Science)
(Spanish)

F. Galishoff (H. 10th Gr. Lit)

NSHS Booster Club

NSHS Football Coaches

Amherst College Football Coaches

Dean/McDonald (Track Coaches)

S. Taylor (Baseball Coach)

I. Seybold (After-School Program)

B. Green (Safety Officer)

M. Bailey (Asst. Principal)

C. Bronzino (8th Art)

Bassett (Art Teacher)

K.Johnston (7th Social Studies)

God Parents

Aunts, Uncles

Cousins

Pastor K. Marcus (Sr. Pastor)

Pastor W. Conner (Youth Pastor)

Church Family

Friends Attending College

S. Freed (Math Tutor)

K. McCord (Professor)

Extended Family

Dr. K. Mason (Pediatrician)

Dr. M. Bassett (Principal)

Positive Peers

T. Carpenter (Track Coach)

I. Snowden (Grandfather)

'Peach' (Grandmother)

Granny 'E' (Grandmother)

Tommy Cho Karate

Safe Community

Neighbors

Parent's Business Associates

W.H. Miller (Author)

Camps, Special Programs

Coaches

Positive Adult Role Models

Tarus (Entrepreneur)

G. Jones (VP/Engineer)

R. McBride (Principal)

D. Smith (Real Estate Agent)

J. Polyne (Engineer)

Nina Wynn (Mom)

Mychal Wynn (Dad)

Jalani Wynn (Brother)

A. Carreker (Retired NFL)

Reverend RC Hall

Ralston (Barber)

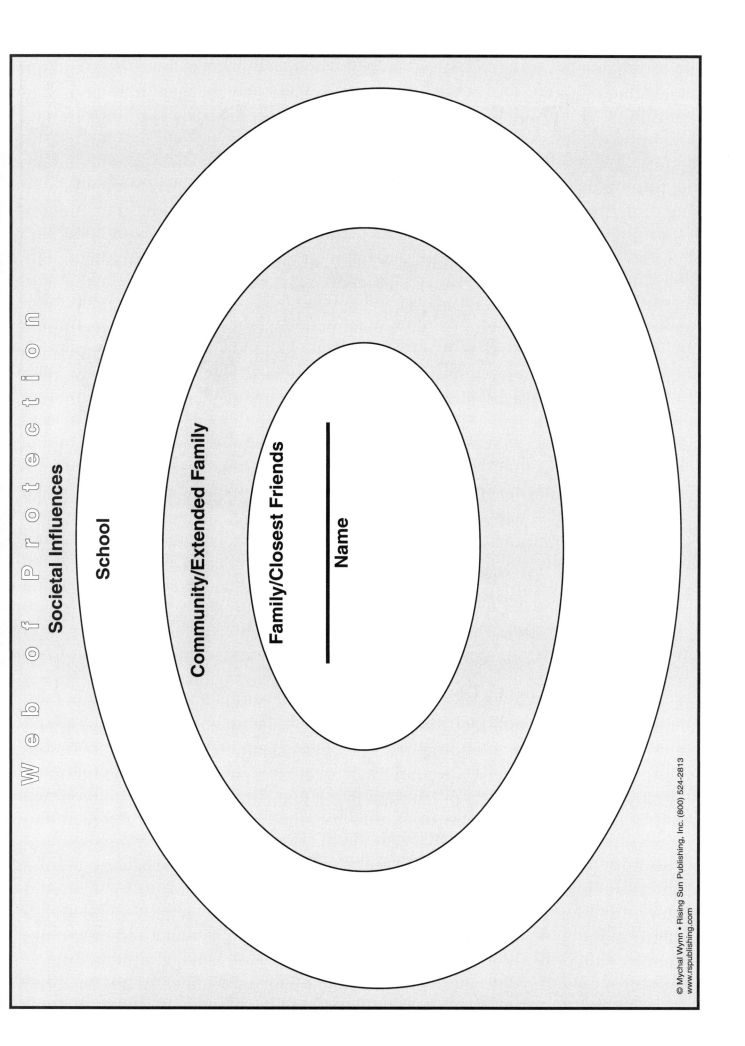

Web of Protection

Societal Influences

School

Community/Extended Family

Family/Closest Friends

Name

A Professional Sports Dream

1. An important exercise is to have aspiring athletes engage in research on several levels:

   a. The sport itself. Such important information would be:

      - average career path, i.e., straight from high school, college, Europe, semi-pro league, or street ball.

      - average career length

      - average salary

      - average agent's commission, state, federal taxes

      - number of teams

      - number of players per team

      - total number of draft picks

      - total number of first round draft picks

      - average rookie salaries

   b. The likelihood of a young man making it into the NBA:

      - from high school

      - from junior college

      - from a Division I, II, or III school

   c. NCAA Requirements for college-athletes

      - get a copy of the NCAA Guide for College-Bound Athletes (www.ncaa.org)

      - prepare a K-12 course schedule

      - prepare a chart of the required grades and test scores

      - review and discuss the college admission and graduation tables

d. Physical Development

- prepare a physical development program with training days, workout routines, and a chart of the major muscle groups being developed

- develop a speed and agility training program

- prepare a nutritional regiment and identify the primary protein sources for muscular development

- identify the process of healing muscle sprains and tears

e. Entrepreneurship and Business Development

- identify the businesses which benefit from professional sports franchises, e.g., concessions, team apparel, parking, security services, referees, television, advertising agencies

- identify the professional services which benefit from professional sports franchises and athletes, e.g., agents, investment bankers, automobile salespersons, real estate agents, attorneys, furniture salespersons, jewelers, house cleaning services

f. An autobiography of his favorite athlete:

- where he attended school

- height, weight, vertical leap, bench press, best physical attribute

- where he was born and grew up

- grades, test scores, college major, best skills outside of basketball

- classes taken, favorite hobbies, other aspirations, family

- describe his character

g. Research the history of basketball and the NBA.

- develop an all-time best team and the personal attributes each player brings to the team

- identify 5 successful former athletes and identify key attributes contributing to their post-NBA success

- identify 5 unsuccessful former athletes and identify key attributes contributing to their post-NBA failure

h. Identify what it would take to enter into any of the basketball related professions (i.e., coach, trainer, team owner, referee, sports analyst, sports journalist)

2. To prepare for life as a professional athlete the young man will have to "process" his research:

a. Prepare questions for potential professionals

- sports agent

- accountant

- financial planner

- insurance agent

- investment banker

b. How will Willie identify competent people whom he can trust with his money?

c. Role play with students who aspire toward these types of careers

3. Have other students who aspire to become journalists, movie producers, television commentators, accountants, or attorneys and have them interview the young man for the following:

a. College admission

b. Professional recruitment

c. Contract negotiations

4. To prepare for life after basketball, Willie will have to research and be prepared to discuss such areas as:

a. The types of businesses he would like to invest in

b. The location he would like to live after retirement

c. The careers he would like to pursue or sports-related jobs that he is interested in (e.g., coach, trainer, sports medicine)

d. The average salaries, education, skills, and experiences needed to pursue such careers

Estimated Probability of Competing in Athletics Beyond High School

Source: http://www.ncaa.org/research/prob_of_competing/

Student-Athletes	Men's Basketball	Women's Basketball	Football	Baseball	Men's Ice Hockey	Men's Soccer
High School Student-Athletes	549,500	456,900	983,600	455,300	29,900	321,400
High School Senior Student-Athletes	157,000	130,500	281,000	130,100	8,500	91,800
NCAA Student-Athletes	15,700	14,400	56,500	25,700	3,700	18,200
NCAA Freshman Roster Positions	4,500	4,100	16,200	7,300	1,100	5,200
NCAA Senior Student-Athletes	3,500	3,200	12,600	5,700	800	4,100
NCAA Student-Athletes Drafted	44	32	250	600	33	76
Percent High School to NCAA	2.9	3.1	5.8	5.6	12.9	5.7
Percent NCAA to Professional	1.3	1.0	2.0	10.5	4.1	1.9
Percent High School to Professional	0.03	0.02	0.09	0.5	0.4	0.08

Related facts:

- Only 3 out of every 100 high school basketball players will play college basketball.

- Only 8 out of every 100,000 will be drafted into the NBA/WNBA.

- Only 6 out of every 100 high school football players will play college football.

- Only 25 out of every 100,000 will be drafted into the NFL.

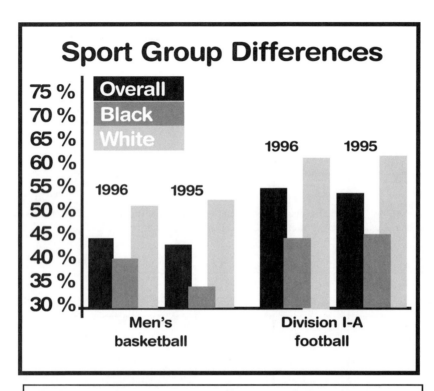

NCAA Division I-A Student-Athlete Graduation Rates

Division I-A football student-athletes in the 1996 cohort graduated at a 54 percent rate, one percentage point higher than the 1995 class but seven percentage points below the 1996 student body. Men's basketball players overall were at 44 percent for the 1996 class compared to 43 percent for 1995. Neither group has graduated at a higher rate than the student body in any year since graduation rates began being tracked with the 1984 class, but both have experienced increases in each of the last two classes. It is also important to note that these groups of student-athletes do tend to graduate at higher rates than their gender and ethnic group counterparts in the student body.

Rates continue to be high in women's basketball, as the 1996 class posted a rate of 66 percent, one percentage point higher than the 1995 group.

[Increasing Student Achievement: Volume I, Vision]

NCAA Student and Student-Athlete Graduation Rates

Source: http://www.ncaa.org/grad_rates/2003/d1/index.html

School	1996-97 All Students	Athletes	Four-year Average All Students	Athletes
Auburn	68	62	67	57
Bethune-Cookman	31	52	35	43
BYU	71	54	72	50
Brown	95	*	94	*
Dartmouth	95	*	94	*
Delaware State	30	54	29	39
Duke	93	88	93	89
Florida A&M	43	46	43	39
Georgetown	94	77	92	87
Georgia Tech	68	63	68	53
Howard	58	62	50	59
Loyola Marymount	70	73	70	68
UCLA	85	64	81	65
UMass Amherst	61	64	60	66
University of Connecticut	69	60	69	62
University of Georgia	70	60	67	64
University of Kentucky	58	48	56	45
Louisiana State	57	55	54	52
University of Miami (FL)	65	51	63	53
University of Michigan	84	82	83	73
UNC (Chapel Hill)	80	64	80	70
USC	76	56	73	61
Northwestern	93	87	92	89
North Carolina A&T	40	23	43	36
Notre Dame	95	92	94	87
Ohio State	59	60	56	59
Penn State	80	80	80	79
Rice	92	81	90	82
Rutgers	72	72	73	68
Syracuse	77	81	75	79
Stanford	93	84	92	87
Texas Tech	52	56	49	55
The Citadel	66	67	68	64
U.S. Air Force Academy	79	*	77	*
Vanderbilt	84	75	83	78
Wake Forest	87	79	87	76
Xavier	71	66	71	74
Yale	95	*	95	*

* Schools do not offer athletic scholarships

What Stories Will You Tell?

Let's take a look at our own storytelling ability and let's take inventory of the stories which we have to tell:

1. Get a journal or notebook. This will become your storytelling journal.

2. Write down some of your most humorous experiences. Things which caused you to laugh at yourself or at other people.

3. List some of your most joyous experiences as a teacher or parent. Describe in as much detail as you can. What made this experience stand out in your mind.

4. List some of your most joyous experiences as a child, then as a young adult, and with your family and friends.

5. List some of your most painful experiences. Of tragedies in your life. Those times when you had great hopes and aspirations and somehow failed to realized your dreams.

These are the stories you're going to begin with. First try to narrate the stories in the third person as though you're talking about the experiences of someone else. Tell the story to a friend or family member. Record the story and replay it to yourself. See if you can gather enough courage to tell your story in the first person. Which stories cause you to laugh or cry?

If telling your story causes others to laugh or cry, then you've told a good story. How did those experiences shape your life? How could others benefit from hearing about those experiences?

For additional stories:

1. Keep your VCR ready to record television programming where people tell stories or jokes.

2. Pick up the audio and video tapes of people who tell stories through training or motivational presentations.

3. Some of the world's best storytellers can be found at your local churches. Pastors really know how to tell a good story with moral and spiritual implications. They wonderfully tie together the challenges, obstacles, and dilemmas of life through their parables.

How You're Smart

[The following example has been reprinted from the book, *Increasing Student Achievement: Volume I, Vision* as an example of how to use student dreams to lead them through a Multiple Intelligences discussion.]

There are many ways to develop relationships with children. In my book, *Building Dreams: Helping Students Discover Their Potential, Parent, Teacher, Mentor Workbook,* I illustrate the power of storytelling as a means of connecting with students:

I have discovered that a well-timed and well-told story or parable can be literally a life-saver when dealing with young people. It quickly grabs their attention in situations where all else seems to fail. It provides a means for the mentor [parent, teacher] to share a lot of personal information and experiences within a relatively short time span and provides a bridge of communication for the mentor to crossover and effectively open dialogue ... Many people don't view themselves as storytellers. Either they simply don't believe that they possess storytelling skills or they don't believe that they have any stories to tell. However, when I work with parents and teachers, they frequently surprise themselves at not only their storytelling ability, but how many stories they have to tell.

At times I may draw upon personal stories about my family, our hopes, and our dreams to make the connection. I use whatever stories or anecdotes I believe can provide a lead-in to discussing their hopes, their dreams, their aspirations, and their attitudes toward school. As I listen to their hopes and dreams, I draw upon my beliefs and experiences to share my insight into ways of achieving what I've heard them articulate as being important to them:

As early as the second grade I had a passion for writing poetry. 'Roses are red, violets are blue, your dog is ugly, and you are too!' My early passion for writing poetry eventually evolved into my dreams of becoming a writer, which eventually evolved into my dreams of starting my own publishing company, which eventually evolved into my dreams of transforming schools into places of passion and purpose where students like you discover and pursue their own dreams.

I don't know what your dreams are, but I do know most of you have already wasted half of this school year. The human brain is the most powerful muscle in your body and most of you have exercised your brains as little as possible this school year. The human brain is composed of billions of neurons which send billions of billions of synaptic signals controlling conscious and unconscious thoughts throughout your lifetime.

Just think, if you'd sat in your chair all school year by now your leg muscles would be so weak you couldn't stand. The same is true of your brains, you've been sitting on them all year!

Now I had their attention. I began asking individual students what their dreams and aspirations were. I took the dreams of each student and created a dream map on the board so they could "see" their dreams weren't impossible, but with their behaviors and their attitudes toward learning, they were certainly improbable:

Of all of the areas relating to your dreams, what have you learned this school year to take you closer to turning your dreams into reality? What have you read about, what have you studied, what have you researched, what have you done to acquire the education needed to achieve your dreams?

The more I talked the more their body language changed as they began listening and thinking. Now I could challenge them:

You say your dream is to play professional football. Okay, list three things you have researched about muscular development and nutrition. What about the difference between animal and plant proteins on muscular development? Why is it important to load up on carbohydrates before practice? Who can tell me the three major muscle groups utilized by offensive linemen as oppose to the three major muscle groups utilized by a running back?

Oh, by the way, how many teams are there in the NFL, how many players are on each team, and what is the average career of a professional football player?

The bad attitudes and smart mouths quickly changed into insightful questions and positive comments. The teacher joined into the discussion, "Mr. Wynn, our community has such few resources, how does a student like Juan follow his dream of becoming a professional boxer when our community doesn't even have a gym?" My response was to illustrate the

Multiple Intelligences identified by Dr. Howard Gardner in his book, *Frames of Mind: The Theory of Multiple Intelligences,* and how Juan could better utilize his experiences in school to expand his intellectual strengths, knowledge base, and subsequently, his opportunities to pursue his dreams and aspirations:

Let's look at the variety of aspects of Juan's dream of becoming a professional boxer and the impact that not having a professional training facility has on his dream.

Juan, since I am not an expert at becoming a professional boxer I can't speak specifically to what you need to do. However, if you and your classmates will help me, we can look at some of the ways that you can become 'smart' enough to achieve your dreams. For example, we know that every person in this classroom can demonstrate intelligence, or be smart, in at least eight different ways. Let's look at some of these ways and how they might relate to a long-term dream of becoming a professional boxer.

Verbal/Linguistic Intelligence *involves being word smart. It deals with effectively talking, reading, and communicating orally and through written forms of communication. For example, how you would articulate yourself in an interview following a fight, your ability to read and understand a contract, and your ability to write and verbally communicate your thoughts.*

Logical/Mathematical Intelligence *involves solving problems. It involves your thinking skills in understanding complex problems and developing a sequence of steps like those typical in math and science. For example, your ability to analyze the fighting style of a boxer you're about to fight and developing an effective strategy. It may also involve rethinking and changing your strategy during the fight itself. It would also relate to developing investment strategies, managing your winnings, and negotiating a contract with a promoter.*

Bodily/Kinesthetic Intelligence *involves effectively using your body. It involves conditioning and training your body to perform well within the confines of a boxing match. This is where your lack of a professional training facility could be a problem. However, a training facility is only one component of enhancing this area of intelligence. It also involves guidance from someone knowledgeable in the sport, a professional trainer. It would also involve understanding muscular development, the difference in eating and training for quickness versus bulk, strength and endurance.*

I went on to discuss the other areas of *Visual/Spatial, Interpersonal, Intrapersonal, Musical/Rhythmic,* and the *Naturalist Intelligences* with Juan and the rest of the classroom. On the chalkboard, I illustrated the types of decisions, strategies, fight preparation, and career choices which would all be impacted by decisions made within each of the intellectual domains.

We were all in agreement that there were many things Juan could do to pursue his dream in spite of the lack of a local training facility. Juan agreed that he was concentrating all of his efforts on developing Bodily/Kinesthetic intelligence and had paid little attention to developing any of the other intelligences, all of which he would come to rely upon, if he was to increase his chances of achieving his dream.

Juan then asked, "Mr. Wynn, if you're a writer, how do you know so much about achieving my dream of becoming a boxer?" To which I responded, "Juan, the cornerstones of how a person follows any dream are: reading, thinking, understanding, planning, and following your plan. All of these are taught or strengthened each day in school. However, you have acknowledged that you have not been applying yourself to developing the skills and acquiring the knowledge available to you each school day. If you are serious about achieving your dreams, then it's time you seriously begin reading, thinking, understanding, and developing your plan. If you truly want to become a boxer, then you must become a thinker."

No more smart mouths. No more negative attitudes. No more disrespectful behaviors. This wasn't an aberration. Developing a relationship and using our beliefs and experiences as a foundation for making a connection between the sterile learning of school and the richness of the world of a child's dreams, hopes, and aspirations opens a doorway to learning both student and teacher may enter together. Taking the time to paint the broad strokes of passion, purpose, and inspiration across the canvas of schooling evolves from internalizing Marva Collins' belief, "*All children are born achievers and all they need is someone to help them become all that they have the potential to become.*"

Remembering from Whence We Came ...

When today's burdens
    appear unbearable
We must remember from whence we came
When today's obstacles
    appear insurmountable
We must remember from whence we came
When today's questions
    appear unanswerable
When the day is full of conflict
    and failing appears inevitable
When we find our courage faltering
    our confidence dwindling
When we find our progress stagnating
    our energy deteriorating
When we find our faith, wavering
    tied to shattered dreams
We must remember from whence we came
We can find the strength to
    bear today's burdens
    overcome today's obstacles
    answer today's questions
And continue confidently
    with unwavering faith
    in search of dreams
Our courage is born of the knowledge
    of how we came into today

                 — Mychal Wynn

The Story of the Bull

There was a man who lived in an area just outside of Los Angeles, California. The man had been struggling with following his dream to become a writer. He had always wanted to write and had in fact written many poems and short stories which he had kept hidden in an old binder. There were many times when he had casually mentioned in conversation with friends and family how he had always wanted to become a professional writer. However, each time he mentioned his dream, he had well-meaning friends, family, and co-workers who were quick to advise him as to why his dreams were unrealistic. They pointed out that he didn't have any professional training as a writer. He didn't know anyone in the publishing business. He didn't have an agent. They told him of other people who they knew with similar dreams who never succeeded. They told him how he really didn't have any spare time with his job, family, and other commitments. He eventually stop talking about his dream and accepted his friends' advice and felt that it was really an impossible dream.

One day the man was visiting a friend who lived in a rural area of Georgia just south of Atlanta. His friend had left his job against the well-meaning advice of family and friends to pursue his dream of becoming a writer as well. His friend was unsuccessful at getting any of the major publishing companies to consider his manuscript. He was in fact a relative unknown and didn't have any professional training as a writer. However, through his perseverance he had successfully formed his own small publishing company and over the course of several years had published four books. Although he still had only a small company with only two employees, he and his wife, he had sold enough books to build his own home and was extremely satisfied with his small company.

While visiting his friend he told him how lucky he was to have succeeded in such a difficult endeavor. But each time his friend attempted to share with him how he could do the same thing, he shook his head and repeated all of the reasons he had heard from others for so long about why he couldn't do it. He was convinced that somehow his friend was more talented, more creative, smarter, or simply luckier. When his friend pointed out all of the things the two of them shared in common and how their lives and circumstances were not so different, his friend finally thought to himself. "You're right, we're not so different. You were just foolish to leave your job and lucky you didn't drag you and your family into poverty!"

Later that day, convinced that his friend was simply foolish and lucky, he stood on the second floor balcony overlooking the backyard watching the children play volleyball. One of the children hit the ball really hard and it bounced over the fence into the adjoining yard. However, in the adjoining yard was a big bull! The fence was so high you couldn't see the bull from where the children were but you could see him clear as day from where he stood on the balcony. The children yelled up to him that they had accidentally hit the ball over the fence and they asked if he would go and get the ball for them!

Well, he looked around for a moment as if to say, "Who me?" Then he looked over the fence at the bull who was standing directly over the ball and the bull looked back over the fence at him as if to say, "Come and get it." It seemed an eternity while he stared at this massive bull, with powerful bulging muscles, long razor sharp horns, weighing at least a ton. This massive one-ton bull was staring back directly at him while the children continued to plead for him to go and get their volleyball.

Well, in that eternal moment before he could graciously tell the children he had no intention of going into a yard with such a massive bull, an elderly man entered through a gate on the far side of the yard where the bull stood guard over the volleyball. The elderly man, who couldn't have weighed more than 140 pounds, entered the yard and walked with his back to the bull over to a small flower garden at the far side of the yard. The bull took his attention away from the ball and turned toward the elderly man and let out a loud snort and began walking quickly toward the man who still had his back to the bull. The old man meanwhile had walked over to his flower garden and got down on his knees and began pruning his flowers, pulling weeds and so forth. Meanwhile from the balcony, he shouted and waved his arms frantically in his attempts to attract the old man's attention. But the old man apparently couldn't hear his frantic screams. He yelled to his friend inside the house to come quick. "Hurry, hurry, we have to call 911." However, before his friend could get out to the balcony, this massive one-ton bull approached the old man and with his huge powerful head nudged the old man in the back, his massive horns surrounding the old man. From the balcony, while frantically screaming for his friend, he saw the old man turn around and with his open hand whack the bull on top of the nose and stopped the bull dead in his tracks. This 140-pound man yelled at this one-ton bull and told the bull to get back over on the other side of the yard! This massive one-ton bull lowered his head and walked back over to the other side of the yard like a little puppy.

As his friend came running out onto the balcony he explained to him what he had just witnessed to which his friend responded, "Is that all?" His friend laughed and slapped him on the back and told him he had a lot in common with the bull. His friend went on to say how despite the bull being a massive and muscular creature, weighing nearly a ton, with razor sharp horns, and possessing the power and potential to reap havoc on the old man and anyone else who would dare enter the yard, the bull had allowed the old man to exercise power and authority over his life. He didn't realize that he was a bull. He didn't realize his power and potential.

The friend went on to tell him how he had been blessed with the gift of writing with a dream to become a professional writer. However, like the bull, he let others exercise power and authority over his life by convincing him he couldn't achieve his dream. Each negative and discouraging comment that they made, and that he accepted, was like that old man whacking the bull on the nose telling him to get back in his place in the corner of the yard. The bull was behaving like a little defenseless puppy not like the powerful, massive creature he was. His friend was acting like he was already defeated as a writer while he hadn't even begun to attempt to realize his potential as a writer.

This story teaches us that while we have power and potential to become more than we are, we allow the problems, events, challenges, and obstacles of life to whack us on the nose and exercise power and authority over our lives.

Washington High School

At Los Angeles' Washington High School, I was invited to speak to students and "motivate them."

Students came in with chips on their shoulders together with all of the negative stereotypical images of urban children. Young ladies with dresses too short and blouses too tight. Young men with their pants hanging around their knees, underwear showing, caps on backwards or sideways, hair uncombed and unclean, big, angry, and intimidating. Not a good picture. There were between 60 to 70 of them. Not to mention the fact they qualified to be here as a result of receiving at least one failing grade on their last report card (although I suspect many of them had more than one failing grade!).

As I was introduced, together with my wonderfully impressive credentials, they showed me just how impressed they were. Some of them put their heads on their desks. Others leaned back in their seats with their hats pulled down over their eyes while others loudly popped their gum as they mumbled about how they didn't want to be there.

The person who introduced me made the fatal mistake of demanding they sit up and pay attention! What a mistake. This only encouraged them to prove that no one could make them pay attention. So they slumped down further into their seats. One six foot nine, two hundred and seventy-five pound young man stood up and said, "I don't want to hear nothing that this man got to say." Before the teacher introducing me could clear her throat and gather her nerve I stepped forward, "The young man has a point. I know you all are tired of people coming in here giving you lectures about what you ought to do. About how you should take school seriously. About how you should study more and get better grades. I promise I am not going to give you a lecture. As a matter of fact, all I'm going to do is to take a few moments and share with you what I'm doing and what I've done. After which, I promise not to bother anyone who doesn't want to be bothered. I promise not to take any longer than five minutes. Is that fair?" As I asked my question, I looked directly at this big, intimidating, 'don't want to be bothered' young man.

I began by asking the question, "How many of you would like to make some money?" A few hands went up. "I mean a whole lot of money?" By then a couple of the heads raised up off of the tables and more hands went up. "Well how many of you want to become writers?" Guess what? No one raised their hand. "But I thought that most of you wanted to make a lot of money?" Then one young man said, "You can't make no money being no writer. Don't nobody read!" A couple of his friends slapped him a high five.

"There was a young man very much like most of you who grew up in a community much like this one. He knew that he wanted to become a writer as early as the second grade, however, nobody thought he could do it. As a matter of fact his high school guidance counselor told him he couldn't make any money as a writer and instead encouraged him to become an engineer."

I went on to share with them how I started out with a dream which had nothing to do with making a lot of money. I just had a dream to realize the special talents which I had been born with. Without telling them how much money I earn, I shared with them my personal story of how I began writing and the income potential of following my dream. This example can be applied to any dream, idea, or career. After I was done all they could see were dollar signs. When I completed the example, I told them that if I could build an entire company from one book of poetry, I could help them develop a plan for whatever it was they wanted to do. In whatever area they felt they had talents or an interest.

I then looked back at the big, intimidating young man and said, "What do you want to be?" He said, "I want to be a computer programmer." I then focused my attention on another student. "A moment ago you said I didn't have anything to say which you wanted to hear. But I've worked as a computer consultant with IBM, one of the world's largest manufacturers of computers. I've been a computer software design engineer with the Transamerica Corporation. I've written computer software in three different computer languages. I even wrote a database management program that is still being used in over 1600 insurance offices throughout the United States. I have a number of friends in influential positions at several Fortune 500 companies in charge of data processing and office automation departments."

With my attention still directed away from the aspiring computer programmer I asked a question of the audience. "Do you think I have some knowledge, information and personal contacts which could help him become a computer programmer?" Of course there were a number of people nodding their heads, some slapping this young man on the back, saying "Yo man, you better check this out." I then refocused my attention on the big young man. "You see, we never know when opportunity is knocking or when the window of opportunity is opening. We can't look at a person and tell who or what they know."

"I promised I wasn't going to give you a lecture. If anyone wants to follow their dream. Or, if you don't have a dream and you want to develop one, then today is your day. I don't care what it is you want for your life. As long as it's not illegal, I will help you to develop your own personal plan. I believe there is greatness within this room. I believe each person in the room has a special gift—something which makes you different. A special talent which no one else has. Well, what I'd like to do is to invite you to join me at the top. To follow your dreams. I will work with anyone who wants to work with me. But I won't bother anyone who doesn't want to be bothered. If you want to follow your dream; if you want to develop your dreams; then join me over on the other side of the room. If you don't have time to follow your dreams; if you just don't want to be bothered; if you don't believe I have anything of value to share with you, then you can stay where you are and wait until the period is over and get on with your life. Even if there is only one person who wants to live his or her dreams, I will work with you."

There was a long moment while they looked around among themselves to see who would be first. You guessed it, the big, intimidating young man stood up first and smiled. As he walked over to the over side of the room all 70 young people followed him.

Storytelling was the first step in bonding. First, through the story I shared one of the examples of how other people can hinder us in achieving our dreams. Then, I bonded through language by sharing a story of success in a nontraditional area. My story just happened to be a personal story. However, there are thousands of stories of people who have overcome the odds to achieve their dreams. After sharing a success story, I further used language to bond by committing to help anyone who had a dream to achieve it and to help anyone who didn't have a dream to develop one.

Next, and most importantly, I gave them the choice to join me. Through the stories, I prepared the way and grabbed their attention. Through my sincerity and commitment to help them, I used language to bond and to embrace them. However, at this point, they had to become self-directed. They had to exercise some control over their future and influence their destinies. We have to have buy-in in order to establish the environment for helping young men to discover their dreams.

We cannot make young men believe in themselves. We cannot make them like each other and stop hating themselves. We cannot make them dream. However, we can establish an environment where positive language is used. Where we don't put each other down. Where it's okay to dream and to share their ideas. Where individual competition is replaced with collective achievement. Where teamwork is valued over selfishness.

Most people don't view themselves as storytellers. Either they simply don't believe they possess storytelling skills or they don't believe they have any stories to tell. However, if you give yourself a chance, you may be surprised at not only your storytelling ability, but how many stories you have to tell.

Passing the Baton

An African-American Student Achievement Club

When reviewing the 'Web of Protection' one of the most notable areas where Black males lack support is in the area of academic achievement. They have easy access to sports teams, booster clubs, after-school programs, and even programs like 'The Gentlemen's Club' which focuses primarily on social skill development. Young men are likely to have a trophy case full of medals, ribbons, plaques, Varsity Letters, and sports trophies and awards. However, they are likely to have very little by way of academic recognition.

The following steps provide the framework for developing a student achievement club. The following resources are recommended:

- *Follow Your Dreams: Lessons That I Learned in School*
- *A Middle School Plan for Students with College-Bound Dreams*
- *A High School Plan for Students with College-Bound Dreams*

1. Using information gathered from the 'College-Bound Dreams' activity, develop sample four-year course schedules which meet college admissions requirements.

2. Using the information gathered from the 'What is Your Mission/Vision' activity, develop a club mission, vision, beliefs, and core values.

3. Using information gathered from the Multiple Intelligences activity, identify the areas of expertise needed. For example, visual intelligences is needed to develop a logo; logical intelligence is needed to develop the rules; and verbal intelligence is needed to develop the mission, vision, core values.

4. Gather student achievement data for African-American students within your school:

    - *Honor roll*
    - *Gifted, honors, AP class enrollment*
    - *Colleges enrolled in (high school)*
    - *Algebra I, chemistry enrollment (refer to statistics of the percentage of students taking these courses who go on to college)*
    - *Special areas of interests, i.e., art, drama, dance, sports, music, law, medicine, or education*
    - *In-school detentions, out-of-school suspensions, expulsions*
    - *High school graduation rates*
    - *College enrollment rates*

5. Identify a faculty advisor.

6. Identify a parent advisor.

7. Identify the founding members.

8. Get a copy of 'Roberts Rules of Order' and elect officers.

9. Develop teams (refer to the book, *A High School Plan for Students with College-Bound Dreams*) with specific areas of focus, e.g., scholarships, developing course schedules, planning field trips, identifying supplemental resources, tutors, trophies, reading list, academic recognition, and/or guest speakers.

10. Identify local resources, i.e., magnet programs, summer camps, after-school programs, art, drama, dance classes, and/or AAU/USATF teams.

Note: The club may be structured as an 'African-American Student Achievement Club' available to both male and female. A special male and female auxiliary may be developed to meet gender-specific needs.

Team Charter

The purpose of a Team Charter is to provide guidelines for team member contributions, conflict resolution, and defining the commitment needed to effectively work together towards the common goal of outstanding academic achievement.

Mission Statement

The team mission is to combine our talents, abilities, skills, knowledge, and efforts toward the successful completion of our assigned tasks.

Guidelines

We will openly communicate among team members when a task is assigned to facilitate its timely completion. The team will assess the individual strengths of team members and assign or volunteer equal areas of responsibility for assignments. Each team member agrees to complete individual tasks in a timely manner and share his or her work with the rest of the team for evaluation and discussion. All team members agree that in order to complete individual tasks, each team member must present and share his or her thoughts, opinions, and ideas with respect and an open mind.

Conflict Resolution

All conflicts will be dealt with in a confidential manner within the team in accordance with the following steps:

1. Investigate the reason for the disagreement.
2. Propose alternative solutions once the source of the disagreement is determined.
3. The team, through a majority vote, must agree on the most appropriate solution.
4. The solution is implemented.
5. Evaluate if the solution is working.
6. Resume the conflict resolution process if conflict still exists.

Results

In order to achieve high levels of performance each team member will ask questions, discuss errors, analyze results, and seek external feedback. The members of the team will be supportive of each other.

Chapter 5

Instruction

Research studies continually emphasize teachers' attitudes and dispositions toward poor achieving minority students in rural schools or urban depressed areas. For instance, Ferguson's extensive meta-analysis (1998) reveals that teachers, both Black and White, almost always have lower expectations for Black students than they do for White students. Arroyo, Road and Drew (1999) as well as The College Board (1999) reached a similar conclusion and go on to note that this way of behaving has an impact on the self-esteem and self-concept of minority students. Thus, the low self-expectations, coupled with teachers' low expectations of them, lead to low performance and achievement.

— Perspectives on Teacher Education Reform

Expectations

While recently at a bid whist party—one of the most common events for Black folks to get together—whether highly-educated or uneducated; a six-figure income or living below the poverty level; working in law enforcement or a career criminal; Ph.D. and high school dropout alike, all types of Black people get together to play cards and talk trash. Highly-educated Black folks can reclaim their roots if they can talk trash and play some cards. While the trash talking is customarily friendly, it can result in 'The Dozens.' Right in the middle of one of the hands of cards, a mother came through the kitchen with her daughter in tow, holding two books:

"Look at my baby, she was recognized in <u>Who's Who Among American High School Students</u> and she made <u>The National Honor Roll</u>. Tell them what you want to be and where you're going to college, honey. That's my baby."

Nowhere is there a greater misunderstanding, miscommunication, and conflict between Black parents and classroom teachers than as it relates to the education of Black children. Black parents want to see their children succeed academically, however, they are less-likely than White parents to have a positive relationship with classroom teachers to ensure that this happens. Black children, who have a good teaching-learning style match and those who can compensate for any mismatches succeed, the others, through each grade level fall further and further behind. Black parents become increasingly frustrated and develop increasingly negative attitudes toward schools and classroom teachers.

Building the bridge between parents and teachers so they are talking about what to do to ensure that Black children are successful academically will do more to close the achievement gap and increase the societal success of Black children in general, and Black males in particular, than perhaps any other single initiative. Building such a bridge begins with understanding the roadblocks between teachers and Black parents and conceptualizing strategies to develop more effective communication and build stronger relationships. In so doing, teachers must keep in mind, as previously outlined in Chapter three, *Climate and Culture*, the communication and relationship may not be with a student's parents but with another influential adult, i.e., aunt, uncle, grandparent, older sibling, coach, pastor, or mentor.

Chapter 5: Key Points

1. Make 'curriculum night' more celebratory and parent-friendly with parent input.

2. Ensure that grading methodology meets student-family needs and is used as an intrinsic motivator rather than as punishment.

3. Don't grade on a curve but establish policies which continually inspire students to complete work and catch up on missing or incomplete work throughout the grading period. Don't forget rewards!

4. Develop a clear syllabus, grading rubrics for tests and major projects, study guides, supplemental materials and all of the necessary information to assist parents in supporting their son's academic achievement.

5. Identify and advise parents of teachers with expertise in multiple intelligences, single-gender classrooms, brain-compatible instruction, learning-styles, and other special needs or instructional areas.

6. Use pre-assessment data for lesson design, to identify tutorial support, materials, and field trips to increase student knowledge and to provide the necessary level of exposure.

7. Utilize Multiple Intelligences grouping to create a collaborative learning environment where student's learn to value each other's intellectual gifts and abilities.

8. Provide frequent opportunities for oral presentations.

9. Learn how to bond with students.

Developing M.I. Teams I

Organize a group of young men into work groups or teams based on their dominant Intelligences, i.e., Verbal, Logical, Interpersonal, Intrapersonal, Musical, Bodily, Visual, or Naturalist. The group sizes should be an odd number, i.e., 3, 5, or 7 with each group member representing a *different* intelligence.

"Let's discuss different types of teams and what they do.

Most of us are familiar with athletic teams. What are some of the types of athletic teams?

Did you know that many businesses form various types of work groups that are made up of different types of people? For example, in the automobile industry, companies form project teams which are responsible for conceiving, designing, building, and selling automobiles. Such groups could be made up of engineers, business managers, marketing managers, assembly-line workers, and automobile dealers.

Other types of business teams are quality control teams who would be responsible for inspecting the finished products and focus groups who would be responsible for comparing different types of products and deciding which ones best meet the consumer's needs.

School districts sometimes create task forces which can be made up of business leaders, teachers, parents, and community leaders who review schools and their curriculum to decide it they best serve the needs of students.

Thus, we are going to organize our classroom into 'Success Teams.' We're going to organize our Success Teams so that we can benefit from the different skills, backgrounds, and individual goals of each person in our class. Just like a football or basketball team, our Success Teams may have superstars, but our primary goal is for the whole team to win!"

Have each team member write his name, multiple intelligence, and career aspiration which would utilize such an intelligence.

Developing M.I. Teams II

Organize a group of young men into work groups or teams based on their dominant Intelligences, i.e., Verbal, Logical, Interpersonal, Intrapersonal, Musical, Bodily, Visual, or Naturalist. Each group member should represent the *same* dominant intelligence.

"Sometimes when we are able to develop teams of individuals with similar talents and abilities they are able to learn from each other, thereby each person on the team develops a stronger ability.

For example, if we had a basketball team and put all of the centers into one group, all of the forwards into another group, and all of the guards into another group each group would compete against each other and each group member would increase his individual skill level.

Competing against the best helps you to become better. The same is true of groups of people where in one group everyone is a scientific thinker, or a group where everyone is a visual artist, or a group where everyone is a good writer.

Based on what you identified as your dominant intelligence, we are going to develop groups of people who are strong within the same area of intelligence."

Analyze the Image

This exercise is designed to raise the consciousness of young men of what to do once they have achieved their dreams.

Identify a professional athlete or entertainer whom you admire and identify the character, values, and personal attributes you most admire about him and why.

If you became a highly-paid athlete or entertainer, how would you answer the following:

1. How will you and your family benefit from your contract?
2. How will your community benefit from your contract?
3. What steps must you take to ensure your fortune is protected and that you continue to reap the financial benefits long after your professional sports or entertainment career is over.
4. Identify the most important subjects for you to study in school and what you need to learn from these subjects to assist you in making the necessary decisions to protect, invest, and ensure that you, your family, and your community benefit from your ability to realize your professional sports or entertainment dreams.
5. What benefits, if any, do you believe a college education can have for a retired professional athlete or a retired entertainer?
6. Identify professional athletes and entertainers who have college degrees and describe how their college degrees have helped them in their business or career.

Backpack Book Club

[Reprinted from the book, *Building Dreams: K-8 Teacher's Guide*].

"Class, we are going to have a club this year called the 'Backpack Book Club.' Everyone in the class is automatically a member because the Backpack Book Club is going to prepare you to become successful.

Each Monday, we are going to post a sign outside of our classroom or write onto the board how many books our class has read during the previous week and how many books our class has read this year. We are going to keep a total for each person in our classroom and for the total number of books that our entire classroom has read.

Reading is perhaps the most important step to preparing us to become successful. It is through reading and comprehension that we are able to learn all of the things that we need to know to become successful.

We are not in competition with each other. Each person needs to do the best he or she can. Whatever you do will count toward the total number of books read by our classroom."

1.   Create a Backpack Book Club bulletin board. Place book covers, topics, etc., onto the board.

2.   Give each student a book chart to keep track of the books read.

3.   Help the students create folders to keep their book charts. These folders can become a reference book by year-end of the books they've read.

4.   Have students tally their books each Monday and note the class total on the board.

Book Log

Date	Title	Parent/Mentor Initial

My Book Report

Name: _____ Date: _____

Title: _____

_____

Author: _____

This book is about: _____

_____

_____

_____

_____

_____

_____

_____

_____

What I thought about this book: _____

_____

_____

_____

_____

_____

_____

Creating a Course Schedule

"One of the most challenging things that you will be forced to do will be to create a schedule of classes that you will take and choose the programs that you will become involved in to help you pursue your dreams and aspirations.

For example, if you have dreams of attending college to study medicine you may have opportunities to choose among a number of math and science classes beginning as early as middle school and through each of your four years of high school. If you have dreams of pursuing a career in professional sports, you may be interested in pursuing classes that focus on physical fitness, nutrition, financial management, or even sports medicine. In addition to the classes that you choose to take in school you may have opportunities to attend summer camps, after-school programs, and participate in a wide range of extracurricular activities.

I'm going to pass out sample high school schedules. The first is for a student who attends a high school where students take four classes each semester. The second is for a student who attends a high school where students take seven classes for the entire school year."

1. Pass out the sample schedules.
2. Engage students in a discussion about their career dreams and interests.
3. Assist students in developing course schedules and identifying camps, programs, and extracurricular activities beginning with the current school year and continuing through high school.

Note: The book, *A High School Plan for Students with College-Bound Dreams*, and your school district's middle and high school course catalog will be helpful in completing this activity.

High School Schedule: 4 x 4 Block
Student Aspirations: Bi-lingual Artist

Middle School	Credit		Credit
Spanish	1		

9th 1st Semester / 2nd Semester

	Credit		Credit
Algebra I	1	Geometry	1
Spanish II	1	Spanish III	1
9th Grade Literature	1	Biology	1
Art Fundamentals	1	2 Dimensional Design	1

10th 1st Semester / 2nd Semester

	Credit		Credit
Honors Algebra II	1	AP Computer Science	1
Honors Spanish IV	1	Honors Pre-Calculus	1
Honors 10th Grade Lit	1	Chemistry	1
3 Dimensional Design	1	Drawing/Painting I/II	1

Online Classes

	Credit		Credit
Honors Economics	.5	Health & Fitness	.5

11th 1st Semester / 2nd Semester

	Credit		Credit
AP US History	.5	AP US History (cont.)	.5
AP Art Drawing	1	Drawing/Painting III/IV	1
AP Spanish Language	1	Honors Spanish Culture	1
Honors American Lit	.5	Honors American Lit (cont.)	.5
Honors Physics	1	Honors Bio/Organic Chemistry	1

Online Classes

	Credit		Credit
Honors Economics II	.5	Health & Fitness II	.5

12th 1st Semester / 2nd Semester

	Credit		Credit
World Studies Symposium	1	AP Statistics	1
Social Studies Elective	1	Elective	1
AP Literature	1	Elective	1
AP Art 3-D	1	Joint Enrollment Art	1

Total Credits Required: 24 • Total Credits Earned: 35

High School Schedule: Traditional 8 Period
Student Aspirations: Attorney

9th

Algebra I
Biology
9th Grade Literature
French I
Forensics
Art
P.E./Health

10th 1st Semester

Honors Algebra II
Honors French II
Honors 10th Grade Literature
Honors Forensics II
AP World History
Honors Chemistry
Music I

11th 1st Semester

AP US History
Honors Physics
Honors French III
Honors 11th Grade Literature
Honors Forensics III
Algebra III/Trigonometry
Music II

12th 1st Semester

Calculus
AP Psychology
AP Literature
AP European History
Internship
Philosophy
Elective
Total Credits Earned: 28

Chapter 6

Assessment

If there is no struggle, there is no progress. Those who profess to favor freedom, and yet deprecate agitation, are men who want crops without plowing up the ground. They want rain without thunder and lightning. They want the ocean without the awful roar of its many waters. This struggle may be a moral one; or it may be a physical one; or it may be both moral and physical; but it must be a struggle. Power concedes nothing without demand.

— *Frederick Douglass*

The area of assessment is far too broad (i.e., authentic, portfolio, grades, standardized tests, and end-of-grade exams) to be covered in any depth. The book, *A High School Plan for Students with College-Bound Dreams,* addresses in sufficient detail the importance of focusing on and preparing for such exams as the SAT, SAT IIs, ACT, AP exams, standardized tests, and high school exit exams and provides worksheets for tracking student exam scores and progress. The area of concern to be explored here, as it relates to Black males, is course grades and the importance of establishing academic goals.

Focus & Identify Goals

Setting goals and assessing strategies is one of the most challenging areas for young men and their families. Some of the reasons are:

- It is difficult to overcome preexisting stereotypes to objectively assess classroom instruction. For example, when Black males are unsuccessful in the classroom the prevailing assumption is they don't care, they're innately lazy, or they lack the intellectual capacity to be successful.

  On deeper study some of the many areas of assessment which could explain classroom failure of teachers and students are:

  - mismatch of teaching- to learning-styles

- cross-generational, cross-gender, cross-cultural, or cross-socioeconomic communication breakdown
- lack of preexisting knowledge in the subject matter
- lack of higher-order or critical-thinking skills
- ineffective note-taking or test preparation skills
- instructional approach relies on least developed areas of intelligence (e.g., verbal and logical versus bodily and interpersonal)

- Overcoming preexisting stereotypes to objectively assess the lack of parental involvement. For example, as alluded to in the previous Chapter, when Black parents don't attend curriculum night, respond to teacher notes, or attend teacher-requested conferences the prevailing assumption is Black parents don't value academic achievement.

  On deeper study some of the many areas of assessment which could explain lack of parental involvement are:

  - parents' negative experiences as a student
  - parents' negative experiences with teachers who used the parents' lack of formal education to degrade or speak condescendingly
  - parents' negative experiences in teacher conferences which seldom affirmed anything positive about their child
  - parents' experiences with teachers who rarely take any ownership of the academic failure of their child and imply subtilely, or overtly, that all failure is attributed to the child's attitude or lack of parental support
  - parent overload, i.e., a single-parent with school children in elementary, middle, and high school while working two jobs
  - parents who are embarrassed by their lack of formal education and their inability to provide at-home academic support
  - parents who are embarrassed by their appearance
  - parents who have a criminal background, outstanding warrants, or are afraid to go to the school

- There may be an unwillingness to assess the overall effectiveness of teacher-controlled practices.

For example:

- Are classroom seating arrangements conducive to reducing personal conflicts and enhancing learning?

- Do grading policies, i.e., homework, pop quizzes, or loss points for failure to include proper headings provide a successful motivator?

- Does grading methodology, i.e., opportunities to turn in late homework for full grade, or opportunities to retake any test (failed or otherwise), motivate or demotivate student effort?

- Measuring effectiveness of discipline practices.

  - Is blind implementation of zero-tolerance policies having the desired effect?

  - Are intervention strategies appropriate and timely in preventing or reducing conflicts?

  - Does out-of-school suspensions and/or in-school detention function as a contributor or detriment to academic achievement?

  - Are discipline infractions occurring at certain times of the day, times of the school year, in particular classrooms, or in particular locations at a predictable rate?

Chapter 6: Key Points

1. Gather classroom achievement data and engage in an ongoing assessment of classroom instruction.

2. Assess parental involvement and survey parents to better understand and meet parent needs.

3. Assess effectiveness of classroom management and identify where student-teacher, student-student, and classroom disruptions occur.

4. Use grading methodology to encourage excellence and to inspire students to submit quality work.

5. Collaborate with parents and mentors to ensure homework is completed and tests and quizzes are adequately prepared for.

6. Build strong parent-teacher relationships.

7. Consciously create a nurturing classroom environment.

8. Inspire students to set personal goals and lead them in developing the necessary kindergarten-through-college plans to achieve their goals.

Set Goals

By having young men identify their goals in extraordinary terms we can begin to help them to see themselves achieving those goals. We must now help them to empower their spirits by affirming their potential. The following affirmation should become a part of their regular routine at home and at school:

1. I am going to YOUR GOAL (e.g., become one of the world's great motivational speakers).

2. I know I have the power to achieve my goals.

3. I know there are many things I must do, but I know I am capable.

4. I know few things that are worthwhile come easy and few things that are easy are worthwhile.

5. I know I will make mistakes, but I will not be discouraged from striving for perfection.

6. I know there will be times when I have only done pretty good, but I will not be discouraged from striving for excellence.

7. I know if I don't quit, I cannot fail.

8. I am going to YOUR GOAL (e.g., become a great speaker).

9. I know I have the power to achieve my goals.

Focusing on Outcomes

1. List every goal on a sheet of paper to be distributed or posted. Write the list so it reads:

    - *Malcolm Robinson is going to become a great educator.*

    - *Robert Smith is going to become a great basketball player and businessman.*

    - *Muhammad Akbar is going to become a great physicist.*

2. Have young men develop a list of fantasy goals, e.g., to become President, a billionaire, to own a million dollar home, or to buy an island in the Caribbean. Encourage them to dream of their highest and most outrageous fantasies.

3. Repeat step one.

4. Select several of the goals from each list and have a discussion identifying the things needed and steps to be taken to achieve the goals on each list. Write down and develop the list of ideas for as long as time permits. Discuss the amount of work, study, diligence and determination required for performing each step.

This discussion should be performed periodically throughout the year. It will help to change the attitudes about their ability to achieve their goals. It will also demonstrate that even goals considered outrageous are achievable when we can identify the steps required to achieve them. Each time this exercise is performed, young men are encouraged to look for solutions to their problems and are being taught how to identify the steps necessary for achieving their goals. It will teach them that their dreams are achievable. Over time their goals will expand and grow in magnitude. Their expectations will grow as will our own. They are becoming empowered!

Reaffirming Your Dreams

Have a classroom discussion about the dreams and aspirations of your students. Ask each student to write down a career aspiration and to list the five most important words or phrases describing how they would need to behave or what they would need to do to achieve their career goal.

Ask for a couple of parent volunteers to meet you after school on a Friday or Saturday morning and do the following:

1. Write down, or print from the computer, the names of each student onto a name card affirming his dreams (e.g., Dr. Smith, Attorney Lewis, Senator Akeem, or Mr. Johnson-Entrepreneur).

2. Place the cards on the front of their desks. Your writing the names or using a computer to print the names on all the cards assures uniformity.

3. Decorate a bulletin board with the words and phrases students identified as being important to the achievement of their dreams.

4. Develop a class schedule from your grade level through the 12th grade consistent with the career aspirations affirmed by your students.

5. Take your morning roll call by addressing students by their title.

6. Begin addressing each student by his or her title as you bring them into the classroom discussions (e.g., the honorable Senator Akeem, what's your opinion on this? Mr. Johnson, what are the economic ramifications of today's events?).

Walk through the classroom calling each of your students by name (Dr. Smith, Mr. Johnson, Senator Akeem) and elaborate on the power and potential of their goals.

"Dr. Smith, you have the power to become a great surgeon. It will be in your lifetime that cures for the incurable diseases of today will be discovered. You have the power to achieve the greatest honor bestowed upon a doctor, the Nobel Peace Prize in medicine."

"Mr. Johnson, you have the power to build a business which will offer employment opportunities to thousands of people. A company which will have the power and resources to rebuild your community. A company which will provide an example of leadership and compassion for the business community throughout the world."

"Senator Akeem, you have the power to become a Senator of the people. To introduce legislation providing opportunities for the homeless, job incentives for Mr. Johnson to open businesses within our inner cities, and to ensure that schools receive enough money so that everyone has access to a quality education."

"Mr. Jones, you have the power to become one of the greatest football players ever, to enter the hall of fame and to own an NFL franchise. You can not only become an outstanding public speaker, but you can provide the example and leadership to inspire other young people to thrive for excellence. To help other young athletes gain the knowledge and skills to become sports analyst, owners, general managers, agents, or entrepreneurs after their careers. To let the world know you can not only score touchdowns, hit home runs, and dunk basketballs, but you can learn complicated offenses and defenses, analyze strategies, and own professional sports teams."

"Attorney Lewis, you have the power to become one of the greatest attorneys and orators the world has ever known. To not only become a partner in a powerful international law firm, but to provide an example of compassion and leadership by defending the rights of those whose resources are limited and whose voices are not heard."

"Mr. Akbar, you have the power to not only teach but to become a great educator. To become an expert in the education and learning-styles of Black children. A teacher of teachers, training others on ways to inspire and encourage young men on to extraordinary levels of achievement."

You see, we can't simply tell young men to get a good education, get a good job, and work hard. Their response is, "Get a job for what; work hard for whom?" We must raise our expectations. Every young man must be encouraged to believe he has the power to become the next great scientist, attorney, astronaut, educator, musician, or whatever he aspires to become. Young men must be inspired to not only know their history but to look wihtin themselves as makers of history.

Decorate a bulletin board with magazine articles, newspaper clippings, book covers, and photographs relating to and reaffirming the goals and careers of your students.

Mychal Wynn · Empowering African-American Males

References

Accelerated Schools Project. (1995). *Accelerated Schools*. Stanford, CA: Stanford University.

Akbar, Na'im. (1991). *Visions for Black Men*. Nashville, TN: Winston-Derek.

Alston, III, J. & Richardson, B. (1991). *Story Power: Talking with Teens in Turbulent Times*. Stamford, CT: Longmeadow Press.

Bell, Janet Cheatham. (1986). *Famous Black Quotations*. Chicago, IL: Sabay.

Boyd, Todd. (2003). *Young, Black, Rich, and Famous*. New York, NY: Doubleday.

Brookover, W., Beady, C., Floor, P., Schweitzer, J., & Wisenbaker, J. (1979). *School Social Systems and Student Achievement: Schools Can Make a Difference*. South Hadley, MA: J.F. Bergin.

Brophy, J.E., & Good, T.L. (1974). *Teacher-Student Relationships: Causes and Consequences*. New York, NY: Holt, Rinehart, and Winston.

Canfield, Jack, & Hansen, Mark Victor. (1993). *Chicken Soup for the Soul*. Deerfield Beach, FL: Health Communications.

Carson, Ben with Murphey, Cecil. (1990). *Gifted Hands: The Ben Carson Story*. Washington, DC: Review and Herald.

Carter, Marlene. (2004). *Just Getting By: Middle Class African American Males Who Are Not Reaching Their Academic Potential*. University Press.

Children's Defense Fund. (May, 2004). *The Road to Dropping Out: Minority Students & Academic Factors Correlated with Failure to Complete High School*. Washington, DC.

Clarke, John Henrik. (1990). *Can African People Save Themselves?* Detroit, MI: Alkebulans.

Cleage, Pearl. (1987). *Deals with the Devil and Other Reasons to Riot*. New York, NY: Ballantine.

Cole, Johnnetta B. (1993). *Straight Talk with America's Sister President*. New York, NY: Doubleday.

Collins, Marva. (1992). *Ordinary Children, Extraordinary Teachers*. Norfolk, VA: Hampton Roads.

Collins, Marva & Tamarkin, Civia. (1982). *Marva Collins' Way*. New York, NY: G.P. Putnam's Sons.

Duncan, Thelma. *(PEP) Los Angeles Unified School District: Proficiency in English Program for Speaker's of 'Black English.'* Los Angeles, CA: Los Angeles Unified Schools.

Dunn, R., Dunn, K., & Treffinger, D. (1992). *Bringing out the Giftedness in your Child*. New York, NY: John Wiley & Sons.

Elliott, Jane. *A Lesson in Bigotry*. http://www.nwrel.org/cfc/newsletters/vol2_is6.asp

Enrollment in Public Elementary and Secondary Schools, by Race/Ethnicity and Locale. (Fall 1999). http://nces.ed.gov/surveys/ruraled/data/Race_Ethnicity.asp

Gardner, Howard. (1983). *Frames of Mind: The Theory of Multiple Intelligences*. New York, NY: Harper and Row.

Gurian, Michael. (2001). *Boys and Girls Learn Differently: A Guide for Teachers and Parents*. San Francisco, CA: Jossey-Bass.

Hale-Benson, Janice. (1986). *Black Children: Their Roots, Culture, and Learning-styles*. Baltimore, MD: Johns Hopkins University Press.

Hare, Julia & Hare, Nathan. (1985). *Bringing the Black Boy to Manhood: The Passage*. San Francisco, CA: Black Think Tank.

Harvard University. (2002). *The Impact of Racial and Ethnic Diversity on Educational Outcomes: Cambridge, MA School District*. Cambridge, MA: The Civil Rights Project.

Harvard University. (2004). *Brown at 50: King's Dream or Plessy's Nightmare?* Cambridge, MA: The Civil Rights Project.

Hilliard, A., Payton-Stewart, L., & Williams, L.O. (1990). *Infusion of African and African-American Content in the School Curriculum*. Morristown, PA: Aaron Press.

Holy Bible. King James Version. Nashville, TN: Winston Publishing.

Hood, Elizabeth F. (1973). *Educating Black Students: Some Basic Issues.* Detroit, MI: Detroit Educational Consultants.

Hrabowski III, F., Greif, G., & Maton, K. (1998). *Beating the Odds: Raising Academically Successful African American Males.* New York, NY: Oxford University Press.

Indiana Education Policy Center. (2000). *Minority Overrepresentation in Indiana's Special Education Programs.* Bloomington, IN: Indiana University.

Johnson & Johnson. (1988). *Motivating Minority Students: Strategies that Work.* Springfield, IL: Thomas Books.

Kennedy, Randall. (2002). *Nigger: The Strange Career of a Troublesome Word.* New York, NY: Vintage Books.

Kohn, Alfie. (1993). *Punished by Rewards.* New York, NY: Houghton Mifflin.

Kunjufu, Jawanza. (1989). *A Talk with Jawanza.* Chicago, IL: African-American Images.

Kunjufu, Jawanza. (1983). *Countering the Conspiracy to Destroy Black Boys, Volume I.* Chicago, IL: African-American Images.

Kunjufu, Jawanza. (1986). *Countering the Conspiracy to Destroy Black Boys, Volume II.* Chicago, IL: African-American Images.

Kunjufu, Jawanza. (1990). *Countering the Conspiracy to Destroy Black Boys, Volume III.* Chicago, IL: African-American Images.

Kunjufu, Jawanza. (1986). *Motivating and Preparing Black Youth to Work.* Chicago, IL: African-American Images.

Kuykendall, Crystal. (1991). Keynote Address: *The High Road to Life.* Atlanta, GA: Wholistic Institute.

Lein, L., Johnson, J.F., & Ragland, M. (1996). Successful Texas School-wide Programs: Research Study Results. Austin, TX: Charles A. Dana Center at the University of Texas at Austin.

Madhubuti, Haki. (1990). *Black Men: Obsolete, Single, Dangerous?* Chicago, IL: Third World Press.

Monroe, Lorraine. (1997). *Nothing's Impossible: Leadership Lessons from Inside and Outside the Classroom.* New York, NY: Random House.

Myers, Isabel Briggs & Myers, Peter. (1990). *Gifts Differing: Understanding Personality Type.* Palo Alto, CA: CPP Books.

National Center for Education Statistics. (1993-1994). *America's Teachers: Profile of a Profession.* U.S. Department of Education.

National Center for Education Statistics. (2001). *Educational Achievement and Black-White Inequality.* U.S. Department of Education.

National Center for Education Statistics. (2003). *Status and Trends in the Education of Blacks.* U.S. Department of Education.

National Center for Education Statistics. (1995). *The Condition of Education, 1994: The Educational Progress of Black Students.* U.S. Department of Education.

National Center for Education Statistics. (2001). *The Condition of Education, 2001.* U.S. Department of Education.

National Center for Learning Disabilities. (April 2003). *Minority Students in Special Education.* New York, NY: NCLD.

National Collegiate Athletic Association. (1997). *NCAA Research Report Characteristics of NCAA Division I Recruits in the 1994-95: Initial-Eligibility Clearinghouse (IEC).* Overland Park, KS: National Collegiate Athletic Association.

No Child Left Behind Act of 2001. (2001). Public Law print of PL 107-110. http://www.ed.gov/policy/elsec/leg/esea02/index.html

Organization for Economic Co-Operation and Development (OECD). (2000). *Reading for Change: Performance and Engagement Across Countries: Results from PISA 2000.* http://www.pisa.oecd.org/

Payne, Ruby K. (1998). *A Framework for Understanding Poverty.* Highlands, TX: RFT Publishing.

Perkins, Useni Eugene. (1990). *Harvesting New Generations: The Positive Development of Black Youth.* Chicago, IL: Third World Press.

Persell, C.H. (1977). *Education and Inequality: The Roots and Results of Stratification in America's Schools.* New York, NY: The Free Press.

Peters, Stephen G. (2001). *Inspired to Learn: Why We Must Give Children Hope.* Marietta, GA: Rising Sun Publishing.

Rothman, Robert. (2001). *Closing the Achievement Gap: How Schools Are Making It Happen.* The Journal of the Annenberg Challenge. Vol. 5, Number 5.

Robinson, Weaver, et. al. (1978). *Beyond Identify: Education and the Future Role of Black Americans.* Ann Arbor, MI: University Microfilms.

Simms, E., O'Neal, B., & Kowalski, C.J. (2004). *Perspectives on Teacher Education Reform: Unique Partnership Initiatives.* Orangeburg, SC: South Carolina State University.

Smiley, Tavis. (2001). *How to Make Black America Better.* New York, NY: Anchor Books.

Smith & Chunn. (1989). *Black Education: A Quest for Equity and Excellence.* New Brunswick, CT: Transaction Publishers.

Southern Illinois University. (2000). *A New Look at the Educational System and Its Impact on the African American Male.* Carbondale, IL: Southern Illinois University.

Star Plan: The Portland Blueprint: Success for Students at Risk. (1989). Portland, OR: Public Schools.

Tatum, Beverly Daniel. (1997). *Why Are All the Black Kids Sitting Together in the Cafeteria?* New York, NY: Basic Books.

Texas Education Agency. (1989). *Effective Schools Research and Dropout Reduction.* Austin, TX: Texas Education Agency.

USA Today. (January 27, 2005). *Ex-high school coach says colleges offered cash for top recruit.* USA Today.

U.S. Department of Commerce, Bureau of the Census. (2003). *Poverty in the United States: 2002.* U.S. Department of Commerce.

U.S. Department of Commerce, Bureau of the Census. (2002). *The Black Population in the United States: March 2002.* U.S. Department of Commerce.

U.S. Department of Education. (1999). *Hope for Urban Education: A Study of Nine High-Performing, High-Poverty, Urban Elementary Schools.* U.S. Department of Education.

U.S. Department of Education White Paper. (October 20, 1997). *Mathematics Equals Opportunity.* U.S. Department of Education.

U.S. Department of Justice. (12/31/03). *Summary Findings of Prison Statistics.* http://www.ojp.usdoj.gov/bjs/prisons.htm

University of Nebraska-Lincoln. (2000). *The Color of Discipline: Sources of Racial and Gender Disproportionality in School Punishment.* Policy research Report #SRS1.

West, Earle H. (1972). *The Black American and Education.* Columbus, OH: Merrill.

Woodson, Carter G. (1933). *The Mis-Education of the Negro.* Associated Publishers.

Wynn, Mychal. (2005). *A High School Plan for Students with College-Bound Dreams.* Marietta, GA: Rising Sun Publishing.

Wynn, Mychal. (2005). *A Middle School Plan for Students with College-Bound Dreams*. Marietta, GA: Rising Sun Publishing.

Wynn, Mychal. (1994). *Building Dreams: Helping Students Discover Their Potential: Teacher, Parent, Mentor Workbook*. Marietta, GA: Rising Sun Publishing.

Wynn, Mychal. (1990). *Don't Quit – Inspirational Poetry*. Marietta, GA: Rising Sun Publishing.

Wynn, Mychal. (2001). *Follow Your Dreams: Lessons That I Learned in School*. Marietta, GA: Rising Sun Publishing.

Wynn, Mychal. (2002). *Increasing Student Achievement: Volume I, Vision*. Marietta, GA: Rising Sun Publishing.

Wynn, Mychal. (2002). *Ten Steps to Helping Your Child Succeed in School*. Marietta, GA: Rising Sun Publishing.

Wynn, Mychal. (2003). *The Eagle Team: A Leadership Curriculum*. Marietta, GA: Rising Sun Publishing.

Wynn, Mychal. (1993). *The Eagles who Thought They were Chickens: A Tale of Discovery*. Marietta, GA: Rising Sun Publishing.

Wynn, Mychal. (1994). *The Eagles who Thought They were Chickens: Student Activity Book*. Marietta, GA: Rising Sun Publishing.

Wynn, Mychal & Blassie, Dee. (1995). *Building Dreams: K-8 Teacher's Guide*. Marietta, GA: Rising Sun Publishing.

1.   Data taken from Bureau of Justice Statistics. *Prison Statistics: Summary Findings (12/31/04)*.

2.   *Ibid.*

3.   *Ibid.*

Films/Video Materials

ABC News (Producer). (1970). *The Eye of the Storm*. New York, NY: ABC Merchandising, Inc., Film Library.

CBS (Producer). (1979). *Marva*. (From 60 Minutes.) New York, NY: Carousel Films, Inc.

Paramount Pictures (Distributor). (2005). *Coach Carter*.

Mentoring Programs

100 Black Men of America, Inc.: http://www.100blackmen.org/

Big Brother Big Sisters: http://www.bbbsa.org

Jack & Jill of American, Inc.: http://www.jack-and-jill.org/

National Urban League: http://www.nul.org/

Young Black Scholars: http://www.youngblackscholars.com/

– Other books from Rising Sun Publishing –

A High School Plan for Students with College-Bound Dreams, [Wynn]
Item #6903 • [ISBN 1-880463-66-0] • $19.95

Easy-to-follow planning guide for high school students. Helps students to understand how grades, standardized tests, behavior, activities, classes, community service, essays, and the billions of available scholarship moneys can all be factored into a plan (beginning in the sixth grade!) that can pave the way into the college(s) of their choice. Provides worksheets for tracking grades, test scores, awards, and class schedules.

A Middle School Plan for Students with College-Bound Dreams [Wynn]
US Version • Item #6901 • [ISBN 1-880463-67-9] • $15.95
Bermudian Version • Item #6902 • [ISBN 1-880463-70-9] • $19.95

Easy-to-follow planning guide for middle school students. Outlines how to maximize the middle school experience and how to prepare students for high school success as a stepping stone to students' college-bound dreams. Provides worksheets for tracking grades, test scores, awards, and class schedules.

Building Dreams: Helping Students Discover Their Potential: Teacher, Parent, Mentor Workbook [Wynn]
Item #5802 • [ISBN 1-880463-42-3] • $15.95

Guides teachers, parents, and mentors through exercises for facilitating discussion and direction for a student or group of students. Mentors learn how to move beyond the rhetoric of lecturing to meaningful and relevant dialogue; dialogue that will facilitate bonding and that will help students focus on long-term outcomes.

Don't Quit [Wynn]
Item #5002 • [ISBN 1-880463-26-1] • $9.95

Mychal Wynn's critically-acclaimed book of poetry contains 26 poems of inspiration and affirmation. Each verse is complemented by an inspiring quotation.

Empowering African-American Males: Teaching, Parenting, and Mentoring Success Black Males [Wynn]
Book • Item #5101 • [ISBN 1-880463-69-5] • $24.95
Workbook • Item #5102 • [ISBN 1-880463-71-7] • $15.95

Black males are the most "at-risk" students in America's schools. They are the most likely to be placed into special education, drop out of school, be suspended, be the victims or perpetrators of violent crimes, or be incarcerated. This book outlines a clear, cohesive set of strategies to turn the tide of underachievement to personal empowerment. Provides national discipline and achievement statistics.

Enough is Enough: The Explosion in Los Angeles [Wynn]
Item #5701 • [ISBN 1-880463-34-2] • $9.95

Provides an introspective analysis of the problems strangling those who live in America's urban battle zones and moves the reader toward solutions to help urban America help itself before it's tool late.

Follow Your Dreams: Lessons That I Learned in School [Wynn]
Item #5003 • [ISBN 1-880463-51-2] • $7.95

All students are confronted with choices during their school-aged years, from kindergarten through college. Which group do I identify with? How seriously do I take my schoolwork? How important is it to establish goals? What are my dreams and aspirations? How can my time in school help me to achieve them?

Mychal Wynn shares his story about the lessons that he learned while grappling with such questions and how he became a high academic achiever along the road to discovering his dreams and aspirations.

Increasing Student Achievement: Volume I, Vision [Wynn]
Item #7901 • [ISBN 1-880463-10-5] • $29.95

This, the first volume of the Increasing Student Achievement series, outlines how a school community goes about the business of developing a clearly-defined commonly-shared vision that drives systemic and sustained efforts toward increasing student achievement.

Inspired to Learn: Why We Must Give Children Hope [Peters]
Item #8901 • [ISBN 1-880463-08-3] • $12.95

Stephen Peters, former middle school principal, not only outlines his vision for the children in our schools, he goes on to share how he and his staff turned their vision into operational strategies.

School Violence...Calming The Storm: A guide to creating a fight-free school environment [Dolan]
Item #7101 • [ISBN 1-880463-14-8] • $29.95

Outlines all of the components and provides everything that a classroom teacher or principal needs to create a fight-free school environment: *instructional lessons; charts; parent communication; letters to the community; classroom, cafeteria, school bus, and school-wide activities; a lesson on the human brain and what causes anger; sample newsletters; fight-free pledge cards; certificates, and more.*

Ten Steps to Helping Your Child Succeed in School: Volume I [Wynn]
Item #7201 • [ISBN 1-880463-50-4] • $9.95

Outlines easy-to-follow steps for parents and teachers to better understand children so that we can better direct them. The steps help parents and teachers to easily identify a child's personality types, learning-styles, Multiple Intelligences, best and worst learning situations, dreams and aspirations.

Test of Faith: A Personal Testimony of God's Grace, Mercy, and Omnipotent Power [Wynn]
Item #6001 • [ISBN 1-880463-09-1] • $9.95

"This book has become more than a recalling of my hospital experiences, it has become a testimony of the power of the human spirit; a testimony of the healing power of the Holy Spirit; and ultimately a personal testimony of my relationship with God, my belief in his anointing, and my trust in his power, grace, and mercy."

The Eagle Team: Leadership Curriculum [Wynn]

Student Guide • Item #7501 • [ISBN 1-880463-66-0] • $15.95
Facilitator's Guide Item • #7502 • [ISBN 1-880463-66-0] • $15.95

An effective intervention and leadership program designed to help unlock the passion within students by leading them through a series of units that will help them to discover their dreams and aspirations as they develop the leadership and academic skills to be recognized as leaders within their respective school communities.

The Eagles who Thought They were Chickens: A Tale of Discovery [Wynn]

Book • Item #5601 • [ISBN 1-880463-12-1] • $4.95
Teacher's Guide • Item #5602 • [ISBN 1-880463-18-0] • $9.95
Student Activity Book • Item #5603 • [ISBN 1-880463-19-9] • $5.95

Chronicles the journey of a great eagle, historically perched at the right hand of the great king in her native Africa, who is captured and taken aboard a slave ship, the eggs that are eventually hatched, and their struggles in the chicken yard where they are scorned and ridiculed for their differences. The story offers parallels to behaviors in classrooms and on school playgrounds where children are teased by schoolyard "chickens" and bullied by schoolyard "roosters."

To order or to inquire about staff development, parent seminars, or student presentations:
770.518.0369 • FAX 770.587.0862 • Toll free 1.800.524.2813
E-mail: info@rspublishing.com • Web site: www.rspublishing.com

This Order May Be Placed By Mail • FAX • Telephone • E-mail
Payment May Be Made By Money Order • Check • Credit Card • Purchase Order

Enter the item number, description, corresponding price, and quantity for each selection (e.g., #1501, Laminated Don't Quit poster, $3.50/ea.) and compute the total for that item. Shipping is 10% of the subtotal (i.e., subtotal of $200.00 x .10 = $20.00 shipping charges). **Allow two weeks for processing.**

Item #	Description (Please Print)	Unit Price	X Quantity	= Total
5101	Empowering African-American Males *Book*	$24.95		
5102	Empowering African-American Males *Workbook*	$ 15.95		
6903	A High School Plan...College-Bound Dreams	$ 19.95		
6901	A Middle School Plan...College-Bound Dreams	$15.95		
7201	Ten Steps to Helping Your Child Succeed in School	$ 9.95		
7901	Increasing Student Achievement: Volume I, Vision	$ 29.95		
5601	The Eagles who Thought They were Chickens: Bk	$ 4.95		
5603	Eagles: Student Activity Book	$ 5.95		
5602	Eagles: Teacher's Guide	$ 9.95		
5003	Follow Your Dreams	$ 7.95		

Method Of Payment
Do Not Send Cash • No C.O.D.s

❑ A check (payable to Rising Sun Publishing) is attached
❑ A purchase order is attached, P.O. # _____
Charge my: ❑ Visa ❑ Mastercard

_____
Account Number   Expiration Date

Signature (*required for credit card purchases*)

SUBTOTAL	$ _____
Shipping (Subtotal x 10%)	_____
Add Handling	3.50
Georgia residents add 6% Sales Tax	_____
DATE: _____ TOTAL	_____

✉ Mail to:
RISING SUN PUBLISHING
P.O. Box 70906
Marietta, GA 30007-0906

RISING SUN
PUBLISHING

☎ Phone toll-free: **1.800.524.2813**
FAX: **1.770.587.0862**
e-mail: orderdesk@rspublishing.com
web site: http://www.rspublishing.com

Ship to (*Please Print*) [Must be same as billing address for credit card purchases]:
Name _____
_____
Address _____
City_____ State_____ Zip _____
Day Phone (_____) _____ Email : _____